Power House
of the
Orleans Rail Road Company,
New Orleans, La.

Ford & Bacon
Engineers.

FOR HUMAN NEEDS

Engineering—Applied science concerned with utilizing inorganic properties of earth, properties of matter, sources of power in nature, and physical forces *for supplying human needs* in the form of structures, machines, manufactured products, precision instruments, industrial organization, the means of lighting, heating, refrigeration, communication, transportation, sanitation and public safety, and other productive work.

Webster's New International Dictionary
G. & C. Merriam Company   1957

FOR
HUMAN NEEDS

THE STORY OF
FORD, BACON & DAVIS

NEW YORK

1967

DEDICATION

This history is dedicated to the founders

Frank Richards Ford
George Wood Bacon
George Henry Davis

whose integrity, vision and professional
competence became a tradition in the
organization they created, and to their
three early partners

Charles Newbold Black
Charles Frederick Uebelacker
William von Phul

who helped them build a business that
over more than 70 years has forged
a record of engineering achievement
recognized throughout the world.

FRANK R. FORD
Partner, 1894–1921
Director, 1921–1930

GEORGE W. BACON
Partner, 1894–1921
Director, 1921–1946
Chairman, 1928–1946

GEORGE H. DAVIS
Partner, 1895–1921
Director, 1921–1942

CHARLES N. BLACK
Partner, 1899–1921
Director, 1921–1928
Vice-President, 1921–1928

CHARLES H. UEBELACKER
Partner, 1899–1921
Director, 1921–1936
Chairman, 1921–1928

WILLIAM VON PHUL
Partner, 1905–1921
Director, 1921–1944
President, 1921–1942

FOREWORD

Building A Future

THE ORGANIZATION that is today known as Ford, Bacon &
Davis was formed in 1894, when the United States was still
busily engaged in digging the foundations for an industrial upsurge that was to bring into being the wealthiest and most productive nation the world has ever known.

From its first major assignment—the electrification of the mule-
powered Orleans Railroad in New Orleans—to its present world-
wide operations, the Ford, Bacon & Davis organization has had a
significant role in building this gigantic industrial complex
which provides the needs and luxuries of a population that,
increasing by nearly 3,000,000 a year, will soon number 200,-
000,000 Americans.

It has been a human achievement, and one in which many
skills participated. Dreamers and businessmen, craftsmen and
mechanics, scientists and teachers, manufacturers and mer-
chants, salesmen, lawyers, accountants were just as important as
the engineers who designed the factories, railroads, power-
houses, pipelines, highways, communications systems, bridges,
dams and other structures which are the man-made sources of
production and wealth.

[13]

The same basic factors that created this American success in the past—enterprise, capital, organization, hard work and the freedom to venture—will govern the coming years.

To see that the story, as it revolved around one important professional group, is available to those who will extend the enterprise into the future, this book has been written from the records of Ford, Bacon & Davis, Inc., and from the recollections of the Ford, Bacon & Davis men who today are carrying forward a long tradition.

In size and world-wide scope, Ford, Bacon & Davis is a larger organization than the founders could have envisioned, but the concept around which they first started the business is the same.

This concept is to obtain, in every assignment regardless of size or cost, optimum results for the client from the minimum investment needed to achieve those results.

CHARLES C. WHITTELSEY

New York
April, 1966

Acknowledgments

For assistance in gathering and verifying data on the expansion of American economic and industrial power in the years since 1894, which is the background against which Ford, Bacon & Davis has grown in size and importance over the years, the co-operation of the following organizations in supplying information is gratefully acknowledged:

Edison Electric Institute   American Gas Association

American Iron & Steel   American Petroleum
   Institute   Institute

Association of American   Automobile Manufacturers
   Railroads   Association

U.S. Department of Commerce

Within our own organization, many hands shared in the research and organization of material from our records and files. Particularly important was the work of Thomas I. Crowell, Jr., who spent a number of busy years organizing the story from its beginnings through 1958. Valuable material was also obtained from papers and articles by George W. Bacon, Charles B. Cooke, Jr., Coleman R. Sample, Page E. Golsan and John J. Delaney. The help of William B. Poor, senior vice-president, in directing the final editorial work, was invaluable.

C.C.W.

Contents

[17]

List of Illustrations

Appendix

1894–1900

I

Trolley Line Construction Jobs
Carry Young Firm to Early Success

I N EVERY YEAR since the dawn of history, there have been com-
pelling reasons for deferring, or better yet, abandoning plans
to start a new business.

Certainly 1894 was no exception.

The nation was still licking deep financial wounds inflicted in
1893 in one of the worst panics in its history. The Pennsylvania
& Reading Railroad had failed in February, and in April the
gold reserves dropped below $100,000,000 as Europe unloaded
American securities for what they would bring. The National
Cordage Co. went bankrupt in May. The bottom dropped out of
the stock market. Business failures were estimated at 15,000.
Some 500 banks suspended payments, and many of them closed
their doors forever.

As 1894 finally arrived, the outlook was totally dismal. Out in
Massilon, Ohio, Jacob S. Coxey was mobilizing an "army" of
jobless men to march on Washington in the spring, demanding a

$500,000,000 poverty program of public works, financed with printing press money which, according to an ancient ritual, "would stimulate business and create jobs."

Strikes, bloodshed and widespread unemployment were to continue through the summer. The famous Pullman strike came in May. Railroad workers struck in sympathy, and President Grover Cleveland called out Federal troops to quell the rioting that broke out in Chicago.

It was to be three long, dreary years, in fact, before the European crop failures of 1897, and demand for American food abroad, brought rising prices and signs of business recovery.

But as George Wood Bacon said nearly 40 years later, in the equally cheerless context of early 1932:

"Today particularly is a time of opportunity for young men . . . Fortunes are not made in boom times. That is merely the collection period. Fortunes are made in depressions, when the wise man overhauls his mind, his methods, his plant and gets in training for the race that is to come."

Instinctively, something along this line must have been in the minds of Bacon, and Frank Richards Ford, fellow-employees of the La Roche Electric Works in Philadelphia, when they were returning to the office for some overtime chores one evening after supper at their favorite rathskeller on Fifth Street, near Chestnut. It was a cold, blustery night in late February, 1894, but they were replete with chops and grilled onions at 35 cents a portion, and between them an intriguing project had taken shape:

"How would you like to go into the engineering business? If we can make money for La Roche, what couldn't we do for 'Ford & Bacon, Engineers.'"

It was to be a lifetime of work together. They delivered their resignations at La Roche the next day, and on March 12, outside a small two-room office upstairs in the Philadelphia National Bank Building, a small, neatly-lettered sign appeared:

FORD & BACON
ENGINEERS

The two partners were well-schooled, well-trained, energetic —and young. Ford, born in Philadelphia and a recent graduate of the University of Pennsylvania, was 22. Bacon, two years older, was an alumnus of Cornell and a native of Greenwich, N.J. Both had degrees as mechanical engineers.

The assets of the new firm, over and above the youth, energy and training of the two partners, consisted initially of $1,000 in cash, contributed in equal shares. Despite the bleak economic climate in which the venture was being launched, these resources proved adequate.

Actually, in 1894, a population of close to 70,000,000 was increasing rapidly as a result of immigration and a high birth rate. President Cleveland vetoed a bill for unlimited coinage of silver bullion. Senator John Sherman of Ohio, brother of the Civil War general and author of the anti-trust law, denounced a proposal for a graduated income tax as "socialism, communism, devilism." The Supreme Court held the law unconstitutional.

By 1895, long before the depression finally ground to a halt, the country was re-grouping its forces for another major economic advance.

The firm of Ford & Bacon planned to move with it. George Henry Davis, a fellow-alumnus of Bacon's at Cornell, was hired during the first year. On July 15, 1895 he became a partner, lending the dignity of his age (32) to the youthful organization, obtaining a one-third interest in its limited tangible resources— and, as events were soon to prove, its unlimited potential. His name went on the stationery and the firm became Ford, Bacon & Davis on January 1, 1897.

Edison's Pearl Street electric power station in New York had been in successful operation since the Fall of 1882. Kerosene and gas were to lose their role as illuminants, but were destined for other vital functions in years to come.

The first oil well had been drilled in 1859. Natural gas was for several years to be an often disastrous nuisance encountered in drilling for oil. Petroleum pipelines, primitive by modern standards, had been operating as gathering and transmission systems for some time, but long-distance, high-pressure transmission of natural gas was still on the drawing board of the future.

Charles Goodyear's process for vulcanizing rubber had founded a shoe business back in 1849. Like petroleum, it was to find its real usefulness years later in the millions of cars and trucks which were to change the face and the pace of America.

Steel production in 1894 had reached a total of some 4,800,000 tons (less than two weeks' output at the 1965 rate) and more was inevitably needed for the job that lay ahead.

The fledgling Bell System had a bare 270,000 telephones on its lines, and was encountering heavy weather against competition as the Bell patents expired. Edison, the electric light some 15 years behind him, was working on motion pictures.

In Europe, an engineer named Rudolph Diesel had invented a new type of extremely powerful and efficient high-compression engine which required no ignition.

Up in Hartford, out in Detroit and elsewhere, something even bigger was afoot which for a number of unrewarding years was to have a resounding popular vote of "no confidence." The bicycle craze was coming to an end and one of the largest makers, Pope Manufacturing Company, by 1895 was turning to a contraption then variously known as a gasoline carriage, road locomotive, and in one case "Buggyaut."

Ransom Eli Olds, Henry Ford, Hiram P. Maxim, Charles and Frank Duryea, Elwood Haynes, Alexander Winton among others were beginning to experiment with different concepts of this new-fangled idea in transportation. Denounced as "harebrained visionaries," many if not most of these men were to become multi-millionaires as a result of their folly.

Meantime, however, the street car industry in which Ford, Bacon & Davis first gained the reputation that in years to come would carry its operations into every state and nearly every country in the world, was embarking on a spectacular expansion. Over the next 20 years, it was to give the nation some 40,000 line miles of cheap, fast, electric-powered transportation.

By the end of World War I, this huge business, reeling from the dual impact of automobiles and buses, was dying. But it left behind it an invaluable legacy of engineering technology in electric generating stations and transmission systems for the power utilities that were soon to become far more important than the trolley had ever been.

One of the major repositories of this technology and know-how was the firm of Ford, Bacon & Davis.

On the same Monday morning that the Ford & Bacon sign appeared outside the small office on the top floor of the Philadelphia National Bank Building, the partners got their first job. The big printing establishment of Allen, Lane & Scott in Philadelphia, which handled among other things the timetables of the Pennsylvania Railroad, was reported to be considering the economics of electric power to operate its plant.

While Ford was out buying equipment for their new office, Bacon went over to the printing plant, gave the layout a fast inspection, and asked to see Mr. Allen. Informed that he was upstairs taking a bath, Mr. Bacon went up and announced himself to a servant.

"Bring him right in," bellowed the printer, splashing vigorously behind a screen which hid him from sight. Mr. Bacon made his first "sales presentation" to the hidden bather, estimating a cost of $40,000 for the job, and a fee of $1,000.

"Done," said the voice from the tub. "Bring me a contract."

The concentrated effort and ingenuity of the partners nursed the job in at $39,500, and the firm had earned its first $1,000. After barebone salaries and expenses, this was to be about a fifth of the first year's earnings.

Eliminating shafts, pullies, belting and other cumbersome, inefficient equipment, the assignment involved the first complete installation of electric power in a printing plant and it also provided the firm with another valuable asset—a satisfied client.

Later in the spring of 1894, came an assignment from the Millville Traction Company of Millville, N.J., which contemplated a few additional miles of electric railway trackage through the city and out to its recreation park on a nearby lake. Beside the extension of track, the job involved a carbarn and a small maintenance shop. Far more important, it involved initial study by the young partners of the engineering and operation of an electric street railway.

The first "big opportunity," however, came in October 1894. As the story was told years later, an impressive, gray-haired man of about 60 appeared at the office, finding Mr. Bacon at a drafting board, alone.

"Do I understand," he asked, "that Ford & Bacon builds electric railroads?" Assured that a recent advertisement in the Street Railway Journal was correct on this point, the visitor introduced himself as Alden McLellan, President of the St. Charles Street Railway Company of New Orleans, and sat down.

After a talk with Mr. Bacon, he invited the firm to submit a bid for electrifying his mule-powered line. It would be necessary for someone to visit New Orleans and inspect the properties— but at the bidder's expense. With minor misgivings fully offset by high hopes, Mr. Bacon accepted the offer and made an appointment, some weeks ahead, to be in New Orleans.

On his return to the office, Mr. Ford was equally enthusiastic about the golden opportunity that the two partners envisioned. Bacon, having had the initial interview, was chosen to make the long trip. However, arriving in New Orleans for the appointment, via upper berth, he found 12 other street railway engineers and builders converged on the city, also invited to bid.

Telegraphic conferences with Partner Ford in Philadelphia led to a joint decision that with Ford & Bacon chances not at all bright they might as well submit a bid which, on the off chance they did get the contract, would yield a fat profit. Mr. Bacon was soon invited to explain the details of their bid to the Directors of the Company, and did so. For Ford & Bacon, this was the end of the St. Charles Street line.

The railroad fare and other expenses of the apparently futile trip began to loom large in the prospect of charging them off to new business which did not materialize. However, fortune, as it turned out, was still smiling on Ford & Bacon.

Paul Capdevielle, the financial head of the Orleans Railroad, another street car operation in the city, having apparently heard favorably of the firm, sent Mr. Bacon an invitation to call. Wasting no time, Mr. Bacon responded, and the two embarked on an inspection trip behind the mules that furnished power for the Orleans transit system.

This accomplished, an estimate of cost for electrification of the line was prepared, which seemed reasonable to Mr. Capdevielle. Mr. Bacon was summoned to appear before the Directors, who immediately engaged in a discussion in French, which was not within Mr. Bacon's field of competence.

It was explained in English that Mr. Bacon seemed to the Board altogether too young a man to be entrusted with such responsibility as electrifying an important street car line. Where was his senior partner?

Mr. Bacon replied that his senior partner was at the moment tied up with vast and complex affairs in Philadelphia, but could and would be able to get to New Orleans in a matter of two or three weeks. Meantime, Bacon said, he would be glad, without obligating the line, to proceed with necessary preliminary studies such as the proper location of their new power plant, carbarns and shops. This economical method of getting the work under way apparently had its appeal to the thrifty directors, who voted in favor of it and forgot to ask Mr. Ford's age.

Three weeks later to the day, Mr. Ford arrived, having been informed of the nature of the impasse by wire:

"Contract in danger because of my youth. Dignity and years essential. Take three weeks grow beard, then come New Orleans confront Board."

As Mr. Bacon told it in later years:

"When Frank stepped off the train in New Orleans, I scarcely knew him. He not only had a fine black pointed beard, but a tall hat, Prince Albert coat, spats and cane. A highly imposing figure, without doubt a man of years and background. And with what poise and dignity did he present to the Directors, our Firm's proposal."

"One look at my elder partner settled the matter, even if he had not handled so masterfully, the advantages of electrification and the further assurances to be gained by having the work done by Ford & Bacon. The contract was ratified by unanimous vote, signed and delivered a few days later."

The electrification of the Orleans Railroad was the beginning for Ford, Bacon & Davis of a long history of successful operations there. When Mr. Davis joined the firm in 1894, it was initially as head of the New Orleans office.

The city was among the first in the United States to adopt electric traction for street railway operation. On their first visit, young Ford and Bacon had surveyed the city's entire street car service, and ultimately, as a result, arranged the purchase of the Canal & Claiborne Railroad Company, another mule-powered line, by the Orleans system.

Next the firm undertook the re-building and re-equipping of the New Orleans & Carrollton Railroad Company. In both these projects, they had the financial backing of the New Orleans banking house of Isidore Newman & Sons, and their engineering

Electrification of the Canal & Claiborne trolley line in New Orleans, and extension of its lines using, in many sections, the street divider or "neutral ground" for tracks, was completed in 1896.

and management services were partly paid for with common stock in the companies.

All over the country, during these years, electric trolleys were replacing horses and mules, just as a generation later the gasoline engine was to replace the trolley. By 1902, only 259 miles were still operated with "animal traction" compared with 5,661 miles in 1890. In the same period, electric power not only supplanted the old horse cars, but stimulated expansion to nearly 22,000 miles of line. This included much suburban and interurban "rapid transit," as these high-speed lines were called.

The transition created a whole new field of engineering, utilizing, adapting and improving power equipment which had only recently been invented—the dynamo in 1882, and the use of the steam turbine to drive it, in 1890.

The engineering mind is nothing if not ingenious. One night in New Orleans, the two partners, Bacon & Davis, were riding to their hotel in a street car and as it speeded around a curve, a large laundress and her basket of clothes lurched into their laps.

Rearranging the distressed lady, they fell to discussing preventive action and the idea of a handle for standees was born. The firm collected royalties for many years from the patent, probably not without thinking of the dictum that "it's the straphangers who pay the dividends," as a trolley magnate of the time was quoted as saying.

Again, it was Davis who conceived the idea of the inverted third rail as a power source where the overhead wire was for any reason impractical.

The work of the young firm was gaining recognition among those who controlled the properties and projects requiring engineering services. The rewards were to be proportionate.

It was in 1895 that the Quaker City National Bank called in Ford & Bacon with a problem concerning a railroad which ran up the Palisades from the New Jersey terminal of the Hudson-125th Street ferry. While horses and mules could negotiate the 12–15% grade, electric motors then available could not.

The firm surveyed the problem, advised acquiring the ferry and running it directly west across the river, rather than two miles northward from 125th Street. Then a new railroad could be built, climbing the Palisades at about a 6% grade en route to Leonia, Englewood, Hackensack, Paterson and eventually Newark and other north Jersey points.

This seemed both logical and prospectively profitable to the bankers, and the firm was retained to do not only the engineering, but the construction and later, to operate and manage the property as well. The deal included an option on common stock of the new railroad.

Thus came into being the New Jersey & Hudson River Railway & Ferry Company—the firm's first really big achievement. In the 12 years from 1895 to 1907, the railroad was conceived, planned, built, owned and operated by Ford, Bacon & Davis. Its eventual sale to Public Service Company of New Jersey was to yield an overall profit on the order of $2,500,000, before, and in those days, after taxes as well.

Frustration is as much a part of the life of the professional engineer as the solid satisfaction of bringing to completion, on time and within projected costs, a major undertaking that represents new wealth and a new productive resource in a world where privation, even today, is never much more than a crop failure or two away.

Following close on the heels of the highly profitable New Jersey & Hudson River project, came a call from Richard A. McCurdy, president of the Mutual Life Insurance Company.

First asking for an opinion on some terminal agreements of the Northern Railroad of New Jersey, he decided to finance the purchase of the property, and retained the firm as consulting engineers for this purpose. Some time later, Ford and Bacon were summoned by McCurdy and given a hand-written letter which read:

Dear Mr. McCurdy:

I have just learned that you are negotiating with some young men, Ford & Bacon by name, for the purchase of the

[31]

controlling interest in the Northern Railroad of New Jersey. This is to advise you that I have my own plans with respect to this Railroad.

Sincerely yours,
J. P. Morgan

Then, with a trace of a smile, he handed them another letter:

Dear Mr. Morgan:

I have your letter of this date by hand and hasten to reply. What you state is true, but let me say at once, it is with deepest regret that I learn at this late date of your plans for the Northern Railroad of New Jersey, since I have already concluded its purchase.

Sincerely yours,
Richard A. McCurdy

Ford & Bacon had already conceived and worked out for McCurdy, through the Fall of 1896 and in early 1897, a plan to bring the Northern of New Jersey into Hoboken, opposite 14th Street, where a ferry owned by the Stevens family of Hoboken would connect it with a New York terminal. Plans called for complete electrification of the road, and a tunnel under Hoboken Hill.

As was not unusual in those days, J. P. Morgan managed to achieve what he set out to do. In subsequent negotiations, he acquired the Northern on behalf of the Erie Railroad, and the plan for the Hoboken–New York extension was abandoned. Ford & Bacon emerged from the transaction without financial loss, substantial gains in terms of business and professional friendships, and a large collection of unused blueprints.

In sharp contrast to world conflicts of later years, the Spanish-American War was brief and definitive. The impact on the nation's economy was negligible in comparison with what future wars would mean. The battleship Maine blew up in Havana harbor February 15, 1898 and by December 10 a peace treaty had been signed in Paris. More men had died of disease than of battle wounds.

That same year, the increasingly-successful firm of Ford, Bacon & Davis moved the headquarters of its expanding business to a New York office at 203 Broadway, in the old Mail and Express Building. The office had been opened two years before, to handle growing responsibilities in the area. New York was fast assuming its position as, for all practical purposes, the business headquarters of the world, and the world was precisely the area in which Ford, Bacon & Davis was planning to operate.

Shortly after the move to New York, the organization became a five-man team with the addition to the staff of two young Princeton graduates—Charles N. Black, class of 1888, and Charles F. Uebelacker, class of 1890. Both were trained electrical engineers with enough practical experience to make them immediately valuable in handling assignments which by then were increasing not only in volume, but in size and importance.

As the century came to a close in 1900, it was still the gaslight era. There were fewer than 8,000 automobiles in the entire country, and probably not more than 10 miles of hard-surface road. By then, Ransom Olds was pioneering in quantity if not mass production of cars (immortalized in song as the Merrie Oldsmobile), in a Detroit plant which shortly burned to the ground and forced a new start in Lansing. In 1899, a once prominent magazine, The Literary Digest, stated categorically:

"The ordinary horseless carriage is at present a luxury for the wealthy, and although its price will probably fall in the future, it will never of course come into as common use as the bicycle."

Even today, the production of 210,000 cars and trucks a week (11,137,000 in 1965) is a little awe-inspiring.

The United States in 1900 was beginning to flex industrial muscles that had been hardened over a tough competitive century. They were about to be used to create more, and more widespread economic well-being than men had ever before dreamed possible.

1901–1910

II

Electric Power Industry Emerges, Giant Offspring of Rapid Transit

T HE 20th century got under way on January 1, 1901 in a period of comfortable prosperity. Stocks and commodity prices were moving up. Industrial activity, down a little from the year before, was steady.

But in more ways than one, it was a "take-off" year for a nation of 76,000,000 people in 45 states spread across 3,000 miles of land rich in almost every resource needed for large-scale production of wealth.

A fabulous decade lay ahead, in which a big nation got bigger, and began to develop the big business needed to handle the big job of feeding, housing, clothing and transporting a rapidly-growing population. And doing it on a scale to which Americans would quickly become accustomed.

Marred by tragedy at the outset—President McKinley died September 14, 1901, eight days after he was shot by a self-styled anarchist in Buffalo—and by another financial panic in 1907, the years through 1910 were to see solid economic growth. The birth rate was high. The flood of immigration, largely from Europe, was rising toward its all-time crest of 1,285,349 in 1907. The year 1901 was the last for more than a decade in which fewer than half a million would arrive from abroad. And by the end of the decade, more than 8,100,000 had passed through Ellis Island and other centers.

For the young Firm of Ford, Bacon & Davis the new century marked a turning point. The early years had brought, not surprisingly, struggle and long days and weeks of hard work to beat out the competition for desirable jobs.

James Gilbert White, Charles A. Stone, Edwin S. Webster, Edwin N. Sanderson, and H. Hobart Porter were other pioneer names, and had founded capable organizations in the years between 1888 and 1896. This kind of competition meant that engineering work, once obtained, had to be brought to successful completion within budgets and time schedules. The future was not bright for any organization that failed to measure up to engineering standards that were already stringent and moving steadily higher.

By 1901, Ford, Bacon & Davis was only seven years old, but its reputation was established far beyond the areas of its early achievements. The Firm, with three or four other top engineering organizations, comprised a select group that gave professional stature to the job of building what was very soon to become, by long odds, the largest industrial nation in history.

Early in 1901, things began to happen. On January 4, J. Pierpont Morgan completed the purchase of Andrew Carnegie's steel properties for $492,000,000 and immediately put them into his newly formed United States Steel Corporation, along with John D. Rockefeller's rich Mesabi iron ore properties and a substantial portion of the other steel fabricating companies in this flourishing industry.

The new Morgan enterprise was capitalized at the unheard-of

sum of $1,500,000,000. Predictably, segments of the academic community and others were shocked, although securities issued by the new giant were soon to become valuable assets in many an educational and philanthropic endowment. President Arthur Twining Hadley of Yale foresaw "an emperor in Washington within 25 years," if public sentiment did not quickly demand Government regulation of such monster enterprises.

As the event proved, U.S. Steel's initial 65% of the market dwindled over the years to 45% by 1914 and some 30% today, while the Corporation itself, having demonstrated a pattern for efficient, low-cost production of steel from mine to customer, continued to grow and prosper with the burgeoning demand for steel that lay ahead.

As though explaining to Professor Hadley what Morgan had in mind, the steel industry expanded its production from 10,000,000 to 24,000,000 tons in the years 1901–1909, providing plenty of business not only for U.S. Steel but for others such as the new Bethlehem Steel Corporation which was put together by Charles M. Schwab in 1904.

It was a significant year in other ways, too.

A glider built by two brothers named Wright crashed at Kittyhawk and sent the stubborn Cleveland bicycle repairmen back to their drawing board for a third try.

It was only six years after Morgan founded U.S. Steel that fabulous Spindletop blew in, for some 20 months the most prolific oil producer ever drilled, and the discovery well that opened up the huge oil and gas reserves of Texas and Louisiana. For the petroleum industry and all the other industries which depend on it, the liquid fuel age was born with Spindletop. It gave sensational assurance that there was a lot more oil where the first billion barrels (total U.S. production through 1900) had come from. It also helped to found Gulf Oil Company, fifth largest in the world today. The vast reserves of oil and gas it revealed were to provide major pipeline and other engineering work for years to come, eventually bringing Ford, Bacon & Davis construction headquarters to their present site in Monroe.

But at the turn of the century, Ford, Bacon & Davis was still busy with trolley lines and their generating facilities. It was to be another 20 years before the growth of the natural gas industry brought the Firm down to the Gulf Coast to assume a key role in the design and construction of the multi-billion-dollar pipeline industry which today provides low cost energy in nearly every section of the country.

One of the Firm's important undertakings in those years was the reconstruction of a street railway and light and power plant at Atlanta, Ga. The management of the properties had not ingratiated itself with the customers, largely as a result of poor service which, in turn, reflected inadequate facilities. The Ford, Bacon & Davis assignment was to bring these facilities up to date, and enlarge them to meet the demands of the growing city.

As was not unusual in those days, there was local opposition to the project, stemming in part from political motives and in part from disagreement on allocation of benefits from the franchises involved. None of this opposition seemed entirely selfless or disinterested, but all of it was highly vocal, threatening to involve the entire job in a storm of public controversy.

Recognizing that it was faced not only with problems of engineering and construction, but with what today would be known as adverse and deteriorating public relations, the Firm first resorted to distribution of handbills to contend with this apparently well-organized opposition.

When this proved inadequate, one of the local newspapers (The Journal) was acquired in order to obtain an effective voice for both sides of the controversy. This solved the problem, and the modernization went on to completion as planned, giving the city the expanded transit and power facilities it needed.

The traction and utility system of the Nashville Railway & Light Company, like others of the time, had been outmoded by fast-moving technology in the new electric power industry. Ford, Bacon & Davis, by now a nationally-recognized authority in the industry, was called in to reconstruct the trolley system, and more important, build a new generating plant to meet rapidly increasing demand for electric power. Having completed the work to the satisfaction of all concerned, the Firm was retained to manage the properties.

Management was still a more or less intuitive art, in which talented men succeeded by instinct rather than by the principles and guide lines that Alfred P. Sloan, Jr., and others were to establish in following years.

Engineers had at least a close working knowledge of the physical properties they had created, what these properties were capable of doing, and how they were intended to operate and perform their functions most efficiently. It was logical that the owners of property, particularly in new and fast-growing industries like urban transit, electric utilities and later other businesses, should turn to the men who designed and built them for help in running them.

It was also common practice in those days to give engineering firms, in part payment for their services, a financial interest in the property they constructed. This had, for the investors, a two-way advantage. It gave the engineers an incentive to outdo themselves in efficient design and sound construction—and it saved substantial cash outlays. Capital, in those days, was not as readily available in large amounts as, thanks to an efficient U.S. investment banking structure, it is today.

As these years went by, Ford, Bacon & Davis was to design, build or modernize a large and valuable group of electric railway and power properties in such cities as New Orleans, Birmingham, Knoxville, Memphis, Little Rock and Houston, in which the Firm had not only continuing management responsibilities but substantial financial interests as well.

Some years later, one of the first big public utility holding companies was to be formed to control Ford, Bacon & Davis properties in five large southern cities. It was to be a source of substantial wealth for the partners when the Firm finally sold these interests in 1915.

Meantime, the Firm's services as a consultant were in demand as a result of its continued success on job assignments, and its steadily-growing professional stature.

In 1902, Armour & Company, prosperous Chicago meat packers, which had been diversifying into public utility properties, found itself with problems in managing these properties and expanding them to keep pace with the growth of the communities they served.

One of these Armour-owned utilities operated transit and power services in Kansas City, Mo., and across the river in Kansas City, Kan. Assigned the job of determining what needed to be done to bring the services into line with the requirements of their communities, Ford, Bacon & Davis undertook an intensive study of the properties and the economic area they served. Charles N. Black was assigned to direct the work, and later, from 1904 to 1907, served as vice-president and general manager of the system.

The study disclosed, as a first step in refinancing and rebuilding the properties into a profitable, modern street car system, the need for a new franchise to replace one which was both obsolete and about to expire.

The problem, beyond that, was one of new construction and new equipment, both for street railroad transportation and for electric power and light. It included bridges and tunnels, underground conduits, trackage and other new railway facilities, as well as new generating facilities and transmission and distribution systems.

The municipal authorities in the two cities had appointed a Committee of 100—a group of outstanding citizens who would see that the public interest was well-served, and at the same time relieve the political authorities of responsibility for whatever might go wrong. After several months of "conferences" (probably more accurately described as haggling), an agreement was hammered out which satisfied both the municipalities and the Armour interests.

The trolley work got under way, with the Firm fully responsible for complete reconstruction of what had been a cable system into a modern, efficient electric railway. It was a major undertaking with, at the peak, some 8,000 to 10,000 men on the Firm's payroll to handle the engineering, purchase of materials and actual construction work.

There was, however, a fly in the ointment. A separate contract had previously been let for a new power plant on the banks of the Kaw River which separates the two communities. The work was nearing completion—the station was built, boilers and generating equipment were in place.

Ford, Bacon & Davis engineers insisted, however, on a thorough examination of the Weather Bureau records. These showed that 42 years before, the Kaw River, swelled by cloudbursts, had risen high enough to innundate the nearly-completed plant and put it out of service indefinitely. Against arguments that "it could never happen again," the Firm's study showed that, on the contrary, it very definitely could happen again, and probably would. The runoff from the watershed, which had been largely stripped of timber in more recent years, was in fact potentially greater than before.

This convinced the Armour interests that they would be well advised to abandon the riverbank site, despite the heavy investment it represented, and relocate their generating station on high ground.

Obligingly, almost as if by prearrangement, about 90 days after the new plant had gone into operation on a site well above the river, a flood, unprecedented in history, came down the Kaw, destroying 22 steel bridges and putting two power plants near the river completely out of commission.

The area might have been without an adequate power supply for close to a year, had it not been for the new Ford, Bacon & Davis station—incidentally, at the time, the largest and most economical generating facility west of the Mississippi.

The event, which stimulated a great deal of discussion among utility people, did nothing to diminish the growing stature of an organization then less than nine years old. They were crowded years and fast becoming more so.

As the business grew, the organization necessarily expanded to handle increasing responsibilities. In 1903, Schuyler C. Stivers became associated with the Firm, bringing with him a broad background of experience in accounting and management, particularly of electric railway properties.

Another important figure in the story of FB&D, William von Phul, a graduate of Tulane University, joined the organization in 1905. He was to become the first president when the Firm was incorporated in 1921.

In 1906, John L. Esson joined the staff, later to specialize in studies and reports covering a wide range of industries in which management needed outside consultation in upgrading operating efficiency, cutting costs and planning for future expansion. Both he and Mr. Stivers were to become vice presidents when the Firm later decided to incorporate the business in order to help assure the continuity that, under a partnership, is sometimes difficult to achieve.

Although commonly, and understandably, engineering accomplishment is measured in terms of steel and concrete structures in place, these physical evidences of achievement represent only a fraction of the professional work involved.

Even before meaningful discussion can start on an engineering project, basic studies and surveys must be made to determine not only the public need for the facility, but the most efficient way to meet the need at the lowest ultimate cost. While in the case of electric utilities, the need might be obvious, the best and most economical way to meet the potential demand in relation to the individual community still had to be determined on the basis of factual studies.

The experience gained in such preliminary appraisal and valuation work in connection with its construction of transit and electric power facilities soon became a valuable professional asset, distinct from the Firm's by now outstanding capability in actual design, construction and operating management.

The impartial nature of these studies, on which bankers relied in financing and re-financing utility properties, was further assured by the fact that the Firm (and later the corporation) has always been owned entirely by its partners and employees, and thus completely independent of possible outside influence. Where in this earlier period the Firm itself had a financial or management interest in properties, conflict of interest, or the possibility of it, was studiously avoided.

A young draftsman was among those hired in these early days, who was to serve the organization for 47 years and make an outstanding contribution to its "public image" and for that matter, to its professional stature as well. Harry T. Cruikshank, who came to the Firm in 1905, was the man who, more than anyone else, evolved the unique typography used for the Firm's name, which is adapted from old English and German script, and designed to convey exactly what the name Ford, Bacon & Davis has come to stand for—a long-established organization of unquestioned professional integrity. It was he who, as final editor of all reports made by the Firm to its clients, was also responsible for the clear, readable format of charts, tables and typed material that add immeasurably to the value of any document or report.

As time passed, its growing prestige was increasingly to involve

Ford, Bacon & Davis in market investigations and reports, impartial appraisals of values in properties and equipment, and recommendations on work needed to bring the properties up to current standards of efficient operating condition.

One of the earlier examples of this type of assignment came to the Firm from the Chicago City Railways, which controlled surface lines on the South Side of Chicago. This report, when completed by a staff under Mr. Uebelacker, included the first studies ever made of "origin and destination of passengers," an essential factor in providing proper urban transit service.

As a result of the work, surface lines in the congested Loop (which is made by the elevated transit system in the heart of Chicago), were re-routed. Later, a traffic analysis by the Firm outlined means to relieve congestion in the Loop itself.

For The Philadelphia Company of Pittsburgh, a similar but far more complex and significant project was undertaken which, when it was completed at the end of 1906, had become the most comprehensive report of its kind on public utility properties that had ever been made. Again, Mr. Uebelacker was in charge.

These Philadelphia Company properties included not only the street railways, but the electric power and artificial and natural gas utilities serving the entire Pittsburgh area. It was, at the time, the largest natural gas business in the country.

This gas business became an extremely significant aspect of the job, since the report necessarily had to include a study of the natural gas properties, including the underground reserves which supplied the fuel.

After completion of this work, a majority of the capital stock of The Philadelphia Company was acquired by the United Railways Investment Company. The principal seller was an inventor named George H. Westinghouse, whose railroad air brake and other devices had made him wealthy and famous some time before the name went on electrical equipment and household appliances.

[44]

The Firm was retained by United Railways as consulting engineer and manager of the Pittsburgh properties, and it also acquired a financial interest in them which was ultimately to prove rewarding. But this was only part of the story.

With what turned out to be the worst possible timing, United Railways Investment in 1905 had acquired, through a wholly-owned subsidiary called United Railroads Company, a cable car transit system in San Francisco.

On April 18, 1906, the most destructive earthquake in U.S. history left San Francisco and the cable car system in fire-blackened ruins. United Railroads Company went from annual earnings of around $1,500,000 to a deficit of around $3,500,000.

Under a management contract with URI, Partner George Davis had been in charge of the San Francisco transit system when the disaster struck. Before the wreckage was cool, an emergency team of FB&D engineers was mobilized and reconstruction was under way which replaced much of the cable with direct electric power.

The power house at Washington and Mason Streets was designed and built as part of this reconstruction and, with various improvements since then, is still furnishing electric power to operate the underground cables that power the cars. The cable machinery, originally operated by steam, was "modernized" with electric power in 1911, while FB&D was still managing the city's transit system. It was during this period, too, that the Firm designed what were believed to be the first pay-as-you-enter cars.

The San Francisco cable cars, operating on the steep hills of the city, have a quadruple braking system—regular wheel brakes, the cable clamp which keeps speed down to nine miles an hour, auxiliary brakes, which are wooden blocks that are depressed against the tracks, and an emergency system which thrusts a metal wedge into the cable slot, and usually requires several hours to release.

Despite the fact that the reconstruction was on a "crash" basis, the Firm was able to re-design and modernize the system while the work was in progress. Studies were also set afoot which soon resulted in a new power generating and distribution system, including the North Beach power station and other facilities.

During this emergency period, the Firm had concentrated its top personnel in San Francisco and, as though there were not enough to keep them busy, the organization decided that low-cost hydroelectric power could serve the city more efficiently and profitably than its existing steam plant.

Further studies were initiated and, as a result, over the next five years, famous Strawberry Dam and a 40,000-kilowatt generating plant were built in the Sierra Mountains and connected with the city by double 110,000-volt transmission lines running 160 miles out of the mountains and across the San Joaquin Valley to connect with the city system.

The Sierra & San Francisco Power Co., which emerged from this project, was a full-fledged electric utility—conceived, engineered, built and then managed and developed as a prospering enterprise by this team of engineers.

The firm, years later, sold its large interest in the property to Pacific Gas & Electric Co. Today, it is an integral part of the nation's biggest power utility system.

Like most other electric power projects of the time, it was built primarily to provide low-cost electricity for the trolley operation and only incidentally to sell electric service to such industrial and retail customers as might be found once the supply was available.

It was the need for cheap transportation that first brought low-cost electric power and light into American cities and created the nucleus around which today's multi-billion-dollar public utility system came into being.

Three years before this huge San Francisco job was completed, came the financial panic of 1907, a banking crisis which swept the nation following the collapse of New York City's

Knickerbocker Trust Co. A group of bankers led by J. P. Morgan obtained $100,000,000 of gold from abroad to shore the Treasury's reserves and thus reversed the downtrend, so that by 1910 business was once more on the mend.

Meantime, while one group of Ford, Bacon & Davis men were working in California, another was equally busy with smaller but important and profitable jobs in the East. A team working under Mr. Ford was in charge of the engineering, design and construction of the powerhouse, track work, overhead power lines and car procurement for the new Coney Island & Brooklyn Railroad Company, the first electric trolley to New York's world-famous amusement park.

In 1909, a valuation was ordered on the properties, for rate-making purposes, in which Ford, Bacon & Davis evolved new concepts which are still imbedded in such procedures—methods of ascertaining overhead charges, and of computing intangible, going-concern values for the purpose of determining a fair return on the investment.

During this period, the Metropolitan Street Railway Company of New York City had gone into bankruptcy and the receivers rightly felt that the property would have to be drastically upgraded in order to operate profitably. By now a recognized authority in all phases of the electric street car business, Ford, Bacon & Davis was assigned the task, with James A. Emery as engineer in charge of the project.

In connection with this project, new designs were developed in carbarns, maintenance and repair shop facilities, and standardized car equipment, which were to be widely adopted by street car systems throughout the country.

About this same time, the City of Philadelphia was aggrieved by allegedly poor management and bad service on the Philadelphia Rapid Transit Company trolleys. Bowing to popular clamor, the Pennsylvania Railroad Commission retained Ford, Bacon & Davis to make a complete and exhaustive study of the property and its operating problems. The objective was, of course, recommendations that would point the way to modern, efficient mass transportation for the city, at minimum cost.

The study, directed by Mr. Ford, took about a year and covered every phase of the operation—traffic, service, equipment, organization and operating methods—on the entire system; which included the Market Street subway-elevated line. The result was a set of findings and recommendations, made in 1913, for new designs in cars, additions to existing service, a new city-wide routing schedule drastically improved over the inefficient one previously in effect, and a wide assortment of other improvements to the system.

Favorably received, the report marked the beginning of a long association between the Firm and its native city, in the study and joint solution of traffic and other engineering problems.

By now, it was 1910. The Firm had grown and prospered. It was a remarkable team of men, whose skills and talents covered not only every phase of engineering, but finance, accounting, sales promotion, administration and other aspects of business as well. Often hundreds and sometimes thousands of miles apart, these men ranged over the country to carry out client assignments, often establishing homes and moving their families to the cities where their technical and business experience was needed.

But despite its increasing size and geographic dispersion, the organization retained, as it does today, the close coordination of varying talents and training that alone makes possible the broad range of services an engineering firm must be able to provide.

New and bigger offices, reflecting the increasing stature and prestige of a large professional organization, were needed. The Firm in 1907 moved to suitably impressive quarters at 115 Broadway where it was to remain for the next 20 years.

The organization had achieved, through sound, conservative practice combined with creative pioneering whenever it was indicated, the professional stature that in following decades was to carry its gothic-lettered name into every part of the world where engineering skills in design, construction and operating know-how were required.

1911–1920

III

World War Brings Hectic Growth,
Firm Expands to Meet Challenge

CAUGHT UP in a war destructive on a scale unprecedented in history, the United States in the decade through 1920 was to bring into being a new dimension of economic power, emerging from the struggle as the world's leading industrial nation.

In 1911, a population of over 92,000,000 was increasing at a rate which would carry the total past the 100,000,000-mark by 1915. William Howard Taft was completing his single term as president when the Supreme Court on May 15 ordered the dissolution of John D. Rockefeller's huge Standard Oil Company, and four days later ordered the break-up of James B. Duke's American Tobacco Company. Both were found to be in "unreasonable restraint of trade." The companies which emerged from these dissolutions went on to far bigger things in markets that are still growing half a century later.

Meantime, in accordance with his assertion that "the man who

[51]

dies rich dies disgraced," Andrew Carnegie was giving away the millions Morgan had paid him for his steel business. Establishment of the Carnegie Corporation as a foundation with an initial endowment of $125,000,000 brought his total philanthropies by the end of 1912 to nearly $200,000,000.

The following year, the 16th Amendment to the Constitution saddled the country with a Federal income tax. And in December, 1913, the Federal Reserve System went into operation, designed to eliminate the recurrent financial panics which for years had plagued a rapidly-growing nation.

By this time, days were numbered for most of the electric transit systems that Ford, Bacon & Davis and others had built during the previous 20 years.

The automobile industry was beginning to move into high gear. Production of cars and trucks, which had reached 100,000 units in 1908, totalled 210,000 as the decade got under way in 1911, heading pell mell toward a record 2,200,000 by 1920. Total vehicle registrations were to jump from 639,000 to 9,239,000 in the same 10 years.

The industry was accused of "glutting the market" as it scored its first 1,000,000-car year in 1916. Spectacular growth had begun after 1911 when Henry M. Leland, founder of Cadillac and later head of the Cadillac Division of General Motors, installed Charles F. Kettering's first practical electric self-starter. Cranking eliminated, only long skirts remained to hamper women drivers, and these were soon to be shortened.

Firmly established as one of the country's ablest and most successful engineering and construction firms, Ford, Bacon & Davis was increasingly involved in impartial studies and appraisals of public utility properties where its professional prestige gave weight and authority to findings and recommendations needed for rate-making.

The Firm in 1910 had made an appraisal for rate-making purposes of the properties of the Union Electric Light & Power Company of St. Louis. Mr. von Phul, who became a partner in 1912, was in charge of the work.

In 1912, a similar valuation and report, including an estimate of going concern values, was completed for Consolidated Gas, Electric Light & Power Company of Baltimore, and used in rate hearings before the city authorities. The assignment was directed by Charles F. Uebelacker, who also became a partner in that year, and was to be the first chairman in 1921.

These were examples of the Ford, Bacon & Davis policy of rotating and diversifying responsibility among its top men, so that they acquired well-rounded experience and avoided the danger of narrow specialization in limited areas of the Firm's increasingly diversified operations.

The two appraisals were also important as early examples of work which, although unspectacular in itself, not only reflected the increasing stature of the Firm but gave it a source of revenue which was to provide valuable stability to the business over the years. More importantly, it provided a badly-needed service to public utility companies seeking to maintain adequate rates against the pressures of the regulatory authorities that were being set up in the various states. It also provided the Firm with a continuing and consistent source of revenue over the years, and helped offset the cyclical nature of most of the other important phases of the business.

In order to handle its increasing responsibilities, the partnership was expanded on July 1, 1912, to include beside Mr. Uebelacker and Mr. von Phul, another Princeton graduate, Charles N. Black, who had joined the organization in 1899, exactly two weeks before Mr. Uebelacker.

As an indication of the rewards the Firm had been able to accumulate in its first 18 years of achievement, the capital of the new partnership was $3,300,000, compared with the $1,000 which Ford and Bacon had scraped together in 1894. The three original partners put up $1,000,000 each, and the three new partners contributed $100,000 apiece. Earnings, however, were allotted between the two groups on a two-for-one basis, since the younger men were expected to carry an increasing share of the Firm's work and responsibility.

Two other important men came to the Firm in 1912— Alexander L. Black, an experienced electric railway engineer, and Charles B. Cooke, a graduate of the University of Pennsylvania, and widely-known as a specialist in public utility and industrial engineering.

In 1912, Ford, Bacon & Davis engineers were back in Philadelphia on a major assignment. A new city administration had taken office, elected partly on the basis of a pledge to give the growing city a modern, properly-coordinated transit system. Appropriately enough, the Firm was retained to make a complete study of its native city's transportation needs and to draw up a basic plan for the rapid transit facilities that would provide adequate and efficient service.

Things went smoothly, under the direction at various times of Mr. Ford, Mr. Uebelacker and James A. Emery, who had joined the firm in 1908, with several years of experience following graduation from Massachusetts Institute of Technology in 1893.

Intensive and detailed studies were made to determine the flow of existing traffic, including the origin and destination of passengers on all public carriers throughout the metropolitan area. The studies included the trend of population in various sections of the city and its suburbs, the impact of rapid transit service on real estate values, the feasibility of each segment of the system from an economic standpoint, and the adequacy of existing services.

On the basis of its findings, the Firm went on to submit proposed designs and preliminary layouts of extensions and modernization, with estimated cost of new construction and reconstruction, potential traffic revenues, operating expenses and financial operating results that could be expected from the new city-wide system.

It was at the time considered to be the most complete and comprehensive study of its kind ever made. While the work was in progress in Philadelphia, additional studies were afoot in other major cities—New York, Chicago, Boston, London, Paris and Berlin—in order to get the benefit of as much past experience as possible in big-city rapid transit—type and amount of service, character, volume and trend of traffic loads, as well as operating methods, financial results, and types of equipment required for maximum efficiency.

This work, and the accumulation of material on which the recommendations were based, produced two fat, fact-packed volumes which were submitted to the city authorities in July, 1913. The recommendations, designed to provide a balanced and comprehensive system, called for four new subway-elevated lines which, together with the existing Market Street subway-elevated line, would provide the service the city needed, and would also provide for future growth as indicated by trends evident at the time.

The report was favorably received, the entire program, submitted to public referendum, got final approval. The city embarked on the construction of the new system. Ford, Bacon & Davis was retained as consulting engineer for a newly-organized Department of City Transit. Two staff engineers, Mr. Emery and Fred K. Merriman, a graduate of Massachusetts Institute of Technology in 1904, were assigned to the job and moved to Philadelphia to work full-time on it. One was responsible for design and construction, the other for traffic, operating plans, finances and operating contracts. Under this supervision, the work was completed as planned and within projected costs. It was one of the last major urban electric transit system jobs to be undertaken for the next 50 years.

It was conceded at the time that, as a result of this and other investigations and reports on urban transit, Ford, Bacon & Davis had probably accumulated the most comprehensive collection of data and statistics on rapid transit systems and operations in the United States, if not the world. Many of the basic principles evolved are still relevant today, as major cities everywhere struggle with the increasing congestion created by cars, buses and trucks using streets and highways never designed for such traffic, and completely inadequate for it.

Untangling transit problems in a crowded city or reclaiming a wilderness for useful production is all in a day's work for the professional engineer.

During the time the Firm was at work on this definitive urban transportation project in Philadelphia, another team of Ford, Bacon & Davis men were equally busy out in a barren area of Montana, where the Valier-Montana Land & Water Co. had decided to explore a major reclamation project which would bring a large area of land into production as farm and pasture, by providing an adequate supply of water.

Mr. Uebelacker had been chosen to direct this challenging project. Following initial studies which confirmed the economic feasibility of the proposed development, definite plans were submitted in 1913. The Birch Creek Dam, highest of its type in the world, was built, and a smaller dam, the St. Francis, was rebuilt. The impounded water, together with flumes and irrigation facilities, created a huge tract of valuable agricultural property out of arid wasteland, at a cost of about $2,500,000.

At this time, the electric transit industry still had a decade ahead of it in which revenues would continue to expand. The lethal competition of highway transportation had not yet become a visible threat. But new construction was tapering off.

Among the last interurban trolley lines to be built in the United States were Ford, Bacon & Davis projects in Scranton and Syracuse. Both were under the supervision of Mr. Ford.

For the Lackawanna & Wyoming Valley Railroad Company, a new system was constructed to provide a high speed, third rail line between Scranton and Wilkes Barre. The work included engineering and design of trackage, powerhouse, car equipment and management of the completed system. The Firm retained a substantial interest in the property for several years.

A similar project was designed and built for the Empire State Railroad Corporation of Syracuse, which also remained under the Firm's management for some time after it was completed. This, in later years, led indirectly to acquisition of large industrial interests in the Syracuse area which were to contribute substantially to the Firm's future prosperity.

These years saw Ford, Bacon & Davis growing steadily—in the size and scope of the work entrusted to it, in the importance of its achievements, and in recognition among the nation's business and financial leaders.

Then, almost without warning, came a new and far bigger challenge than ever before.

The assassination of the Austrian Archduke Francis Ferdinand at Sarajevo on June 28, 1914, seemed at first an isolated tragedy. But through that summer, war spread across Europe. Germany and later Turkey joined with Austria, while England, France and Russia allied themselves against this formidable and initially successful combination known as the Central Powers.

The impact on the United States was almost immediate and completely without precedent as the Allied nations sought to buy arms, ammunition and everything else needed to supplement their own production, and support the huge armies that were rapidly being mobilized.

The American response, first in production, and later in

military action, left the world in awe. A new industrial power had come into being, and one which no other single nation could any longer hope to match.

Steel production soared from 23,500,000 tons in 1914 to 44,400,000 tons by 1918. In the same years, total exports went from $2,330,000,000 to well over $6,000,000,000 and continued upward through 1920 when they passed an unheard of $8,000,000,000—a peak not to be seen again until a second major war engulfed the world in 1941.

Engineers and builders necessarily were responsible for the breakneck pace of industrial expansion which made possible this gigantic achievement. Ford, Bacon & Davis, swamped with urgent tasks, went on a round-the-clock work schedule, seven days a week. Not the least of the Firm's contributions was a personal one. Mr. Bacon was appointed acting head of the Export Department of J. P. Morgan & Co., during the absence in Europe of Edward R. Stettinius, a Morgan partner.

The Morgan banking firm had been retained by the three major Allied powers—England, France and Russia—to handle procurement in the United States of huge quantities of munitions, food and other vital supplies.

J. P. Morgan & Co., which had close connections with British banking and business interests going back many years, was delegated to handle this multi-billion-dollar purchasing job shortly after the war started. It was late in 1914 that Mr. Bacon was asked to assume day-to-day direction of the work involved.

Moving to the Morgan offices at the corner of Broad and Wall Streets, he functioned mainly through Lloyd George, later British prime minister, but then minister of munitions. In addition, there were three separate missions of about 20 men each, representing the three Allied governments in New York, working earnestly as advisors, but doing little to simplify Mr. Bacon's pressing and highly-complex task.

The work got done, under Mr. Bacon's direction until July, 1916, when Col. Black relieved Mr. Bacon of his nerve-wracking assignment, and directed the program until the mission was substantially completed in January, 1918.

Some $3,500,000,000 worth of munitions, equipment and supplies had been procured, paid for and delivered to the Allied Forces under this arrangement, in which the Firm's extensive administrative and engineering resources were pressed into service as required to accomplish the job.

German leaders have long since conceded that it was this deluge of U.S. production which completely upset their calculations. No one at the time believed, until it became an accomplished fact, that such tremendous quantities of material could be produced and shipped to the beleaguered Allies in so short a space of time.

Not only did this production enable them to stave off the initial German thrust, but it provided the momentum from which the United States could launch its own full-scale participation. When Congress formally declared war on April 6, 1917, American industry had been working around the clock for well over two years.

Production, already at capacity levels in most industries, had to be stepped up even more—quickly, and at any cost. Like others, the Ford, Bacon & Davis organization met the challenge and took on an even heavier work-load as the nation set about the job of mobilizing a huge army, training and shipping it to Europe and then supplying it with food, clothing, weapons and ammunition.

One of the first of these additional assignments came from the Platt Iron Works of Dayton, which retained the Firm to supervise a major expansion of its plants to produce some mysterious device. The Firm quickly completed the facilities and was retained to help manage initial production of what turned out to

Early trolley line construction gave FB&D a reputation in New Orleans. The huge New Orleans Harbor Board grain elevator (at top) was built before World War I. The even larger U.S. Army Supply Base (above) was designed and built in 1918.

[60]

be the building of the still new and, at the time, fantastically powerful military weapon—tanks.

The job was in charge of Harold V. Coes, a graduate of Massachusetts Institute of Technology who had joined the Firm in 1917, and was later a founder of the Association of Consulting Management Engineers, and president of the American Society of Mechanical Engineers.

Crude and unreliable by modern standards, these first American tanks were a potent weapon in their day, and had a vital role in breaking the stalemate of trench warfare which, for nearly three bloody years, had threatened to prolong the hostilities in Europe indefinitely. The Platt works met the nearly impossible schedules which had been set up for initial production.

While this was going on, another team of Ford, Bacon & Davis men, headed by Mr. Davis, was dispatched to Clinchfield, Va., as consultants on design and construction of a new coke plant to produce smokeless fuel for the Navy, and at the same time to supply huge quantities of toluol for the powerful explosive TNT. This was essential for artillery and naval ammunition, and in bombs for a fledgling air force. Once more, the job came in on schedule.

The problem in World War I, as again in the conflict which was to come some 20-odd years later, was not just the production in unprecedented quantities of arms, ammunition and supplies, but of moving this material to Europe across a submarine-infested ocean. This involved not only shipping, but major terminal facilities. Neither existed.

A third Ford, Bacon & Davis team, under George I. Rhodes, another MIT graduate who had joined the Firm in 1917, was assigned to Richmond, Va., to design and build, in what again proved to be record time, a plant to manufacture steam boilers for the new ships which were soon to be launched by the U.S. Shipping Board's Emergency Fleet Corporation. The boilers were ready for them as needed.

Down in New Orleans, meantime, still another Ford, Bacon &
Davis group, led by Frank J. Trelease, a graduate of Washington
University, St. Louis, in 1908, was engaged in design and construction for the War Department, of a $15,000,000 Army
Supply Base, including concrete warehouses, wharves, railroad
yards and loading facilities. The job, completed ahead of schedule, was in familiar territory since, some year before, Ford,
Bacon & Davis had completed a major port construction program for the New Orleans Board of Commissioners. On this
job, FB&D hired a young engineer, just out of school, named
Cornelius van den Berg, who immediately impressed his supe-
riors with unusual energy and ability. He was later to become
vice-chairman and a director of Southern Natural Gas Company,
and one of a number of FB&D men who have, from time to time,
by mutual agreement, joined client organizations where their
talents were needed.

As though all this were not enough to keep the organization
busy, the Firm, late in 1917, was assigned what was then the
biggest construction job in its history—the building of a
$68,000,000 smokeless powder plant at Nitro, West Va. It
was to be the largest of its kind, and Mr. Davis and Mr.
Uebelacker took charge of the construction. Using, at the peak, a
work force of some 40,000 men, the Firm completed the project
in the 10-month period from January to October, 1918. The
plant had been in production about a month before the Armi-
stice was signed.

In the perspective of history, it was the procurement mission
for the Allies, first under Mr. Bacon and then under Col. Black,
which helped to throw American industry into high gear and to
gain the momentum of all-out production that later made possible the nation's own rapid military and naval build-up.

The heart of the performance was know-how—in manufacturing and in the engineering required to design and build,

practically overnight, the facilities to harness and channel the productive energy of nearly 100,000,000 people.

Looking back on those years, it is certain that this vast flow of arms and supplies from the United States was crucial in turning back Germany's early bid for victory, and enabling the Allies to survive until America threw a crushing weight of fresh manpower into the struggle, and ended it.

The diversion of the Firm's operations into industrial design and construction, as a result of wartime demands on its resources, turned out to be far more significant than could have been apparent at the time. It was a field that would not only take the place of the electric railways which had dominated the Firm's activities in earlier years, but would provide a far broader and more rewarding challenge to its capabilities.

The trolley industry had reached a peak, in size, of 45,000 track miles in 1917, but continued to grow in revenues for several more years. Not until 1922 did the long decline set in that by 1960 left less than a tenth of this trackage in operation, concentrated in a few large cities.

Buses and private cars gradually took over the transit job, and in years to come were to create new problems of urban congestion that threatened to choke the crowded business districts of nearly all the larger cities of the nation.

Today, this congestion, which apparently is only compounded by complex superhighway systems surrounding major cities, promises a revival of electric-powered rail transit as the more efficient, economical method of moving masses of people between their city jobs and their suburban homes. A new 75-mile system is already under construction to serve the San Francisco–Oakland metropolitan area. Atlanta has a project under way and other crowded cities are studying similar solutions to worsening traffic problems.

In mid-summer, 1965, Congressional action authorized a new

$431,000,000 subway-surface rail transit program for the District of Columbia, to be completed by 1971.

Nearly 50 years ago, when the big electric transit industry began to give way to buses and automobiles, Ford, Bacon & Davis could list more than 20 large cities in which it had done major work on street railway properties, and in most cases on the electric power stations which were a part of them.

Starting back in New Orleans, the Firm moved successively on such assignments to Philadelphia, Elmira, Atlanta, Washington, Kansas City, Birmingham, Nashville, Little Rock, Knoxville, Memphis, San Francisco, Chicago, Toledo, Pittsburgh, New York, Jersey City, Waterloo, Akron, Richmond, Duluth and Superior.

At one time or another in this period, Ford, Bacon & Davis designed and built, modernized or did other important work for more than a third of the trolley industry as measured in track-miles, and in this work helped to create the nucleus of power generating facilities around which a large segment of today's huge electric utility industry came into being.

Despite the leadership they had achieved in this industry, the partners were not slow to recognize the coming impact of automobiles, buses, and of the highway construction these vehicles required. Their holdings in American Cities Company, which owned and operated electric railways and power companies in a number of southern and southwestern cities, had been sold to Electric Bond & Share as far back as 1915. At the time, the American Cities operating companies had annual revenues of some $15,000,000 and included a number of properties which would grow into extremely large and valuable electric power utilities in years to come.

Using the hard-won experience of the war years as a base, in 1917 the Firm began to diversify its resources and capabilities in order to provide manufacturing industries, as it had the transit and power utilities, with a broad range of engineering and economic services.

A staff was organized which was qualified to cope with such specifically industrial problems as optimum location of plants, design of efficient facilities, power, transportation and water requirements, economical handling of raw materials, specialized machinery and equipment and the other engineering factors that bear on low-cost production.

Obviously, these were problems that could be handled properly only in relation to distribution and marketing of the products involved. This led to the formation of a group of specialists in marketing, a move which not only broadened and strengthened the Firm's capabilities in plant feasibility studies, but in itself provided a new and valuable service to clients.

A highly important aspect of this expansion into industrial areas involved valuations and appraisals, in principle similar to those made for public utilities in rate cases, but in practice, vastly different. A new fund of technology had to be created.

Gradually, over the years, a service organization like Ford, Bacon & Davis acquires, through its diversified assignments, a huge volume of information and factual data which is not elsewhere available. This material provides a detailed and specific record of past experience and accomplishment which is invaluable background for dealing with new challenges—whether in engineering and construction or in appraisals and valuations, market surveys, feasibility studies on proposed expansion, or any of the countless other ways in which professional engineers counsel and consult with management in decision-making which requires specialized knowledge and training.

For this reason, complete records, properly classified and indexed, have long been almost a fetish at Ford, Bacon & Davis, and they are in constant use. Like all files, however, they can produce occasional frustration. One of the partners, delayed for a time in locating some old but badly-wanted material, was told shortly afterward that "we can find complete data in these files of ours on practically anything."

"Yes," he said, "eventually."

A separate valuation department was established in 1917, which took over the experienced personnel and data accumulated in public utility appraisal work, and proceeded to build a flourishing business in determining reproduction costs, insurable values and fair market values of all types of industrial properties, as well as utilities.

It was in June, 1918, that James F. Towers, graduate of Georgia Institute of Technology and an engineer who had specialized in work for the steel industry, joined the firm to concentrate on this new industrial appraisal and valuation business. His success in developing the Firm's leadership in what proved to be a widely-needed and valuable engineering service is implicit in the fact that 24 years later, Mr. Towers was to become the second president of the organization.

The Firm was able to bring unusual, if not unique, qualifications to its appraisal and valuation work. Its widely diversified engineering talent was thoroughly experienced in design and construction of nearly every type of industrial or transportation facility, and in the operation of these facilities after they were built. This provided a close working knowledge of original and replacement costs, depreciation and other factors which affect value at a given time.

In 1919, came an assignment, then the largest ever received of its kind—an evaluation of the Philadelphia, Pittsburgh and Franklin plants, and other properties, of the Atlantic Refining Company, now Atlantic Richfield Co. A crew of up to 60 men was engaged in the project during the months it was under way, directed by Winfred E. Reynolds, a graduate of Rensselaer Polytechnic Institute who had joined the Firm in 1918.

This experience was almost immediately put to good use

when, in the following year, an even larger appraisal was required by Standard Oil Company of California. Ford, Bacon & Davis was given the job, and again Mr. Reynolds was in charge. A crew of up to 100 engineers worked through the year, evaluating Calso's far-flung assets—producing, refining, transportation and marketing facilities, as well as the company's large oil and gas reserves. It provided the company with an impartial, third-party appraisal of all its assets, as a basis for depreciation charges and other financial record-keeping which would have a bearing on the financing of future growth.

The potential water shortage which overtook New York City in 1965 was not new in history. Back in 1919, the Government of Greece asked Mr. Bacon to come there to make a survey and report for Premier Venezelos, on providing a suitable and adequate water supply for the city of Athens and its Piraeus seaport. This he did, providing a basis for future development of the ancient city's reservoir and water distribution system which serves it well today.

A similar public service project, in which the Firm at this time played a major part, was the creation of the Port of New York Authority. Since 1917, Mr. Ford had been one of the six members of the old New York–New Jersey Port and Harbor Development Commission, and for many years had been a widely-known expert on public service facilities.

Against this background, he was able to make major contributions to the 500-page report by the Port and Harbor Development Commission, late in 1920, which provided the basis for the creation of the present Port of New York Authority, today one of the largest and most important bodies of its kind in the world.

Scarcely noticed at the time, John Henry Parr, a trained librarian, was hired in 1920 to organize and index the growing collection of books, periodicals, inactive files and other material which had been accumulating since the early days in Philadelphia. For 15 years, Mr. Parr worked at least six and more often seven days a week, setting up a Library of Congress classification of books, demanding appropriations for more books and periodicals, and establishing a voluminous file to preserve in orderly, accessible form, the news stories, magazine articles, technical papers and other material which flowed into the library under arrangements he set up.

Today, as a result of Mr. Parr's labors, Ford, Bacon & Davis has one of the largest private engineering and technical libraries in New York, if not the world. It comprises some 20,000 books, largely of a technical nature and many of them rare, along with back-issue files of upward of 100 professional and other periodicals. Everything is completely indexed and cross-indexed for quick retrieval of current as well as background information on an era which, starting with the electrification of the horse-car, is now concerned with the forms of energy that will move men and machines in the year 2000 and beyond.

As the decade drew to a close in 1920, the Firm embarked on a rewarding venture, for its own account, that was to have far-reaching importance in strengthening the nation's industrial defense and in helping to create today's unchallenged world supremacy of the U.S. aviation industry.

Their interest stimulated by wartime developments, the partners decided to underwrite a thorough study of air transport and aircraft manufacturing, in an effort to evaluate what seemed to be a tremendous potential for the future. This was by no means a pioneering move, but it was made against a background of solid experience that augured for more realistic and perhaps more accurate findings than were currently available elsewhere.

As a result of this internally-sponsored study, the Firm came up with some extremely impressive findings, among them the fact that larger and more reliable planes than were then available could readily be designed and built, and that such equipment would immediately make possible fast, efficient, economical air transportation of passengers and, eventually, freight.

The next step was to bring to this country, at the Firm's expense, a very successful Dutch designer and builder named Anthony Herman Gerard Fokker, who had produced outstanding fighter planes for the Germans during the recent war, and was the inventor of, among other things, the equipment which made it possible to synchronize machine gun fire through a propeller in flight.

Fokker, whose design leadership in aircraft development also included the tractor propeller, as distinct from the pusher installation widely used on early planes, was and still is recognized as one of the great figures in the early history of aviation.

Around him, the partners of the Firm formed Atlantic Aircraft Corporation, to build a new Fokker three-engine plane, which for its time proved to be a sound piece of equipment. The venture continued under Ford, Bacon & Davis management until it was sold to General Motors and consolidated with General Aviation, which, in turn, was sold by General Motors in 1933, to become part of today's huge North American Aviation Corporation, one of the nation's largest aircraft, missile and space equipment manufacturers.

Aside from its important contribution to the development of U.S. aviation, the venture was extremely profitable, and became the first of several successful industrial ventures conceived, organized and managed by Ford, Bacon & Davis over the years. The pattern was much the same as that established earlier in the transit and utility industry.

Over and above the substantial cash returns realized from these ventures, they were perhaps even more valuable as background and in prestige, proving to clients and prospective clients that the Firm's technical, engineering and management know-how was completely practical, and produced results in actual business operations.

1921–1930

IV

Boom Years See More Expansion
Before Long Depression Sets In

AMERICAN INDUSTRY grew rapidly in the decade of the 1920's, its solid gains in capacity and efficiency obscured by a monumental "boom-and-bust" in the security markets.

Behind the facade of speakeasies, jazz and frenzied speculation in stocks, engineers and businessmen were hard at work. The result was new and bigger factories, an increasing volume of production, and a steadily rising standard of living for more Americans than ever before.

From 1920 to 1930, the population went from less than 107,-000,000 to 123,000,000. The economy expanded even faster, and the Ford, Bacon & Davis organization was busy. Growth over the years had reached a point where the partnership was no longer an adequate form of organization for a business which, increasingly active and successful in a number of important areas, must plan for its long-range future.

Accordingly, in December, 1921, it became Ford, Bacon & Davis, Inc., with the six partners as members of the board of directors. Mr. Uebelacker became chairman, Mr. von Phul president, and Charles N. Black vice-president. The three founding partners, retaining a large and active interest in the business, had turned over its day-to-day management to younger but thoroughly seasoned men.

Then, as now, all the stock was owned by active officers, directors, and key employees, and by agreement could not be transferred to others. Because of the highly professional nature of the business, particularly in feasibility, valuation and other studies involving very large sums of money, a policy of internal ownership was established, assuring complete freedom from any implication of outside influence.

The surge in business activity and commodity prices that followed the close of World War I came to an abrupt halt in 1921. There was a short period of acute liquidation. In the stock market, the Dow Jones industrial averages fell from a peak in November, 1919, of 119.62 to a low of 63.90 in August, 1921. This was the base for the almost uninterrupted climb which pushed the average to an unheard-of 386.1 in early September, 1929, a level not to be seen again for 25 years.

The automobile industry was beginning to take shape as smaller producers dropped out or were absorbed by larger companies. Chrysler Corporation was incorporated in 1925, and appraisals of properties that went into the new giant were made by Ford, Bacon & Davis. General Motors, destined to be the largest and most profitable industrial enterprise in the world, had been incorporated in 1916, taking over from a predecessor company organized in 1908. Motor vehicle production went from 2,200,000 cars and trucks in 1920 to 5,300,000 in 1929, a record that was to stand for 20 years. Meantime the total number of motor vehicles on U.S. highways would increase from 9,200,000 in 1920 to 26,500,000 at the end of 1930.

Largely for this reason, the oil business too was growing rapidly, with crude production moving from 442,929,000 barrels in 1920 to over a billion in 1929. The natural gas industry, which had been expanding slowly through the earlier years of the 1900's, marketed only 818 billion cubic feet by 1920. In 1923, however, it crossed the trillion mark, and sales nearly doubled in the next seven years to 1,979 bcf in 1930. The industry was headed toward the key position it occupies today— supplying about a third of total U.S. energy requirements from a complex of plant and pipelines valued at $27 billion, rivaling railroads and highways as one of the nation's major transportation systems.

Steel output, reflecting the growth of many industries, totalled a record 420,000,000 tons in the decade of the 1920's, and installed capacity in the mills went from 60,000,000 to 71,000,-000 tons a year.

New industries were coming into being. Aluminum production in 1922 was less than 75,000 pounds. There were about 400,000 radio sets in use and annual production topped 100,000. Broadcasting was becoming an important business, expanding from a single station in 1920 to over 600 by 1930. Telephones in service increased steadily to 20,000,000 in 1930, up 50 per cent from the 13,300,000 in use in 1920.

Electric transit was still a major industry, and in 1923 carried an all-time record of 15,650,000 passengers. But basic and far-reaching changes were under way.

Most electric traction systems had their own generating and distribution facilities, and this phase of their business was growing rapidly. Production of electric power, which had more than doubled in the previous 10 years, doubled again in the 1920's from 56.5 to 114.6 billion kilowatt hours.

Installed capacity, to meet this soaring demand, was increased from 19,400,000 kilowatts in 1920 to over 40,000,000 by 1930. The concept of the public utility holding company had taken shape, based initially on the perfectly sound idea that a group of operating companies could in this way obtain more efficient central management, legal, technical, purchasing and accounting services than would otherwise be possible. However, unsound and, in a few cases, shady financing, including the public sale of badly over-priced securities, was laying the basis for restrictive holding company legislation in the 1930's.

In 1924, control of the United Railways & Investment Company was bought in the open market by the H. M. Byllesby interests. The United operating companies, most of them originally designed and built, or rebuilt and modernized by Ford, Bacon & Davis, included The Philadelphia Company, Pittsburgh Railways Company, Duquesne Light Company, Consolidated Gas Company of Pittsburgh, and on the West Coast, United Railroads of San Francisco, Sierra & San Francisco Power Company, Coast Valleys Gas & Electric Company and the Market Street Railway Company.

The decline of the trolley industry, and the sale of its own transit and utility properties, meant that Ford, Bacon & Davis had to turn more aggressively to other fields for its future growth. And, in fact, an urgent need for all types of engineering service was fast developing in a wide range of industries.

The organization had fully anticipated this development and was prepared for the transition. Long, successful experience in serving growth-minded, profit-oriented clients, and a tradition steeped in sound engineering practice, proved just as valuable in coming years as in those gone by.

While public utility jobs did not become a major part of its work during these years, several large power projects were designed and built that represented outstanding examples, at the time, of optimum results in terms of minimum capital investment in relation to capacity and operating costs.

An example was the design of the Sterlington, La., steam electric power station built and enlarged under the Firm's supervision, in 1924–1927, for the Louisiana Power Company, a subsidiary of Arkansas Power & Light Company. It was one of a number of projects handled by the firm for Arkansas Power and its subsidiaries during this period, including its Pine Bluff dam.

Because of its proximity to low-cost natural gas, the Sterlington project provided an opportunity to apply a new design concept which combined low first cost and very high efficiency in terms of fuel consumption per unit of output. Not only did the gas-fired boilers use cheap fuel, but they required minimum supervision and no expensive fuel handling equipment.

Completed in 1926, Remel Dam and powerhouse on the Quachita River, designed and built by FB&D for Arkansas Light & Power Company at Pine Bluff, Ark., cost $2,000,000 including a 70-foot concrete dam, 900 feet long.

The results were extremely satisfactory to the owner. The Firm was also assigned the work of designing and building high-voltage transmission lines from the new station 20 miles to Crossett, Ark., and 10 miles to Bastrop, La., including a number of sub-stations connecting with local distribution systems, and a tie-in with Mississippi Power Company at Vicksburg. The work, which was largely under the supervision of Harry E. Whitaker, graduate of MIT and later a vice-president and chief engineer, involved a total of some $8,000,000 including some later expansions.

Pipelines, the most efficient method for long-distance movement of gas or fluids in large volume, by 1920 totalled 55,000 miles of cross-country transmission mains, excluding gathering and distribution systems. During the next ten years, another 33,000 miles would be laid, no small part of it by Ford, Bacon & Davis. In fact, although its capabilities, its operations and its achievements actually covered a very broad range of engineering work, the firm became widely known as "pipeliners"—much in the same way as it had for years been closely identified with the electric railway and power industry.

One of the first construction jobs in this burgeoning industry was an assignment from Northwestern Utilities, Ltd., Edmonton, Alberta, to design, construct and operate a natural gas line from the Viking gas field in Alberta, 77 miles to Edmonton, then the most northerly city in North America without gas service.

With construction under way in the early summer of 1923, the project was completed in late October of the same year, with Edgar G. Hill, graduate of Sheffield Scientific School at Yale, in charge of the work. It was one of the earliest, if not the first, modern, high-pressure system in the world, and included a gathering system at the field and an 80-mile distribution system. The total capital investment was nearly $5,000,000.

This was an early example of the so-called "turnkey" contract, under which the contractor is responsible not only for design and construction of the project, but for placing the completed facilities in full operation, with a permanent organization of engineering, technical and other staff personnel.

Only after the Viking project was in full operation, performing efficiently and delivering gas to customers in the quantity scheduled, was the property delivered to the owner. Over the years, more and more FB&D clients have found this turn-key service valuable, particularly where their own staff could not be readily expanded to assume the added, and often unfamiliar, responsibilities.

Turn-key service has in many cases also had the advantage of concentrating in a single organization the total responsibility for start-up and break-in following completion of a project, so that the owner takes over a going operation, fully organized and performing at rates and costs specified in the original planning.

In this way, the same engineers who designed and built the facilities have had time to remove the inevitable "bugs" and train a competent operating staff.

Shortly after completion of the Viking-Edmonton project, the Firm was retained by Standard Oil Company of New Jersey and the other owners, to make a comprehensive study and report on the big Monroe, La., natural gas field. Following the intensive exploratory work essential in this type of assignment, the Firm determined that the huge reserves in the field would support major development involving a very substantial capital investment.

Accordingly, a long-range plan was presented to the owners, proposing lines to major population centers, with large pipe diameters to operate under high pressure. The first big project based on the Monroe reserves was undertaken for Interstate Natural Gas Co., Inc., and Southern Gas & Fuel Co., in 1926.

It involved design and construction of what was at the time the longest large-diameter natural gas pipeline in the United States. An initial 170 miles of 22-inch line was built to Baton Rouge, at a cost of nearly $12,000,000. This was later connected with New Orleans by an additional 88 miles of 18-inch pipe, which cost about $3,700,000.

The construction went through low, swampy terrain. New methods were evolved for moving heavy equipment along the route, and to obtain solid footing for the line itself. Not the least of the engineering problems was that of putting the first natural gas pipeline across the Mississippi River, anchoring it against shifting currents and flood conditions—and accomplishing the job without interfering with river navigation.

Again, on completion of the construction, Ford, Bacon & Davis was retained to manage the new property for several years before turning it over to the owners. George I. Rhodes, who became a vice-president of the Company about this time, was credited with a number of important technical advances in the design of high-pressure gas lines, which were developed and first applied on this project. He was later to be vice-president, chief engineer and a director.

It was in the late 1920's that Ford, Bacon & Davis built long, large-diameter, high-pressure lines from the Monroe gas fields to St. Louis and Memphis. The St. Louis project, for the Mississippi River Fuel Corp., was a 433-mile line of 22-inch pipe. The other, for Memphis Natural Gas Co., was an 18-inch line 210 miles long.

Pipeline work remained a major phase of the Firm's business through these years, as this highly-efficient method of transportation continued to grow. Several factors stimulated this expansion—primarily the discovery of huge, proved reserves of natural gas, and the fact that gas provides energy in highly-concentrated form, is inexpensive, and can be moved and utilized efficiently and economically as compared with other sources of heat and power.

A number of Ford, Bacon & Davis men shared responsibility for the Firm's work in this specialized field, and for the outstanding reputation which it early acquired as a result of on-time completions, within and sometimes below estimated costs. These included Edgar G. Hill, George I. Rhodes, Frank J. Trelease, F. H. Lerch, Jr., and Charles C. Whittelsey.

The development of the big Amarillo field in the Texas Panhandle provided an assignment to Ford, Bacon & Davis for the construction of some 450 miles of line to Pueblo and Denver, about half of it 22-inch, the rest 20-inch and 16-inch pipe. Canadian River Gas Co. owned the property in Texas, while the sections in New Mexico and Colorado were owned by Colorado Interstate Gas Co. The entire system was managed for the two owners by Ford, Bacon & Davis for many years.

Even larger was the 22- and 20-inch main transmission line built at this time for Southern Natural Gas Co., running from the Monroe field to Birmingham and Atlanta. It involved some 800 miles of high-pressure pipe and cost about $23,000,000. Ford, Bacon & Davis became an important stockholder of Southern Natural Gas as a result of this assignment, and it proved a rewarding investment.

Pipe lining methods, back in the 1920's, were by modern standards, primitive, requiring much human labor since supplanted by mechanized equipment. Above, an FB&D gang makes a river-crossing for a line from Monroe 433 miles north to St. Louis.

The Firm also participated in the construction of a long line connecting the Amarillo field with the big Chicago industrial market, part of a system created by Natural Gas Pipeline Company of America. Ford, Bacon & Davis built two sections. The first, in 1930, was a 140-mile segment of 24-inch pipe from Pawnee to Cloud County, Kans. The second, built in the following year, ran 155 miles across Illinois from the Mississippi River to a point near Joliet.

With continued advances in pipeline technology, particularly for gas under high pressure, it became feasible to use this low-cost transportation for moving gasoline and other volatile refined products over long distances.

One of the earliest of these product pipelines was built in the late 1920's for the Phillips Pipe Line Company, a subsidiary of the big oil company with headquarters at Bartlesville, Okla. Ford, Bacon & Davis supervised construction of this project, which was an 8-inch pipe carrying refined gasoline some 750 miles from Borger, Tex., to St. Louis. For control and protective purposes, a telephone line was installed along the route at the same time. The project cost $18,250,000.

During the mid-1920's, an office was established in Chicago to provide a base for growing Ford, Bacon & Davis operations in the midwest, and to establish business connections close to this rapidly-expanding concentration of industrial activity.

The overall business was evolving into several clearly-defined areas, logically developed out of past experience, and the organization was well-staffed to handle all of them. While engineering design and construction was still largely in the public utility field, it was during the early 1920's that the Company started working for major industrial clients, handling a broad range of projects requiring specialized engineering capabilities.

An important segment of the business was management, usually of specific properties for a varying period of time following completion of design and construction. In a number of cases, this activity was for the Firm's own account, involving properties which it owned or in which it had a substantial ownership interest.

Impartial valuations and reports, originally concentrated in utility rate cases before regulatory authorities, were also an increasingly important phase of the business, no longer confined to electric and gas utilities. Other industries required such services, usually in connection with proposed mergers or underwriting of new securities—often both. Meantime, post-war inflation and the need for higher rates stimulated an increasing volume of assignments from all types of regulated businesses.

In 1921, a valuation was made for Hope Natural Gas Company, a subsidiary of Standard Oil of New Jersey, covering all its producing, transmission and distribution properties in West Virginia. The following year, a similar study was made for another subsidiary, East Ohio Gas Company, followed by an appraisal for Peoples Natural Gas Company, also owned by Standard Oil of New Jersey. In later years, re-appraisals of these properties were required which, along with testimony before regulatory authorities, was to occupy a large staff of engineers for a long period of time.

Hope Natural Gas, now part of the Consolidated Natural Gas system, is famous in the industry as the loser in an historic court battle in which the U.S. Supreme Court in 1940 upheld the Federal Power Commission in its assertion that original cost less depreciation, rather than reproduction cost, was a proper basis for determining fair and reasonable rates.

During this period, the Firm was named to arbitrate a dispute between the City of New York and the Interborough Rapid Transit Company and, in 1923, made appraisals of various IRT subsidiaries which were required in court proceedings.

Ford, Bacon & Davis records show that, by this time, it had made impartial appraisals for various purposes, of properties valued at more than $4,000,000,000, most of them utilities of one kind or another. Since the Firm had designed, built and operated transit, electric power and gas utilities in practically every section of the country, it was increasingly sought out as a qualified and impartial expert in determining fair values for this type of property.

[81]

Because of this impressive background, industrial valuation work continued to develop in volume. In 1921, for example, a valuation was requested by Union Carbide and Carbon Corporation, as it was then known, covering something over 100 different operating and other properties in the United States and Canada, many of them very large. Completion of the work apparently met with the approval of the Company, since it proved to be the first of a long series of assignments given to Ford, Bacon & Davis by Union Carbide, covering nearly every type of engineering service.

Similar industrial assignments were an important source of business through the 1920's. Among them was a valuation of the various properties being merged to form the Pennsylvania-Dixie Cement Corporation. The report was made to the National City Company, then the securities affiliate of the present First National City Bank of New York.

A major valuation was undertaken in 1929 of the properties of Sinclair Oil Corporation, which included an appraisal of future earning power and other intangible values inherent in a going business of this nature. Winfred E. Reynolds and Coleman R. Sample, later FB&D vice presidents, directed the work, which involved a multi-million dollar complex of production, refining and transportation facilities in the United States and abroad. Mr. Sample was a graduate of Purdue University.

In the same year, 1929, the famous "muskrat census" was made. A Louisiana enterprise, Acme Land & Fur Company, needed a realistic estimate of the potential resources of muskrat fur on a tract of some 124,000 acres of swampland. Two Ford, Bacon & Davis engineers, both veteran woodsmen and hunters in their spare time, were soon sloshing through the swamp in hip boots, counting noses and seeking to compute the potential annual "take" from organized trapping. The final estimate was a gross catch of 1,440,000 skins in the first trapping season on the 194-square mile area surveyed.

It was during the 1920's that buses began to replace electric street cars as a more flexible and economical means of providing service. This brought Ford, Bacon & Davis back to some of the cities where they had originally built the first trolley systems. Feasibility studies were needed which would provide a basis for investment in new equipment by establishing realistic projections of traffic potentials and earning power. These and other facts were required to enable transit operators to apply for new franchises from regulatory authorities and make an orderly transition to motor coach service in their territories.

Largely under the direction of Mr. Emery, major studies and reports of this kind were made for the Fifth Avenue Coach Company in New York and the Chicago Motor Coach Company, among a number of others.

Because of the continuing expansion of hard-surface streets and highways and the rapid growth of automobile traffic during these years, a large number of toll bridge projects were set afoot in nearly every section of the country. For many of them, Ford, Bacon & Davis was retained to make feasibility studies, of which a large proportion were negative. Of those which did prove attractive in terms of potential revenue, the Firm received its share of design and construction jobs.

The biggest of these was the New Orleans Pontchartrain Bridge, built in 1928, at a cost of $4,300,000. It consisted of five miles of concrete pile trestle, two steel bascule drawspans, and 10 miles of approaches, providing a reinforced concrete highway over the lake. The bridge was designed to relieve congestion on the state-operated ferries. However, the state first eliminatd tolls on the ferries, and a few years later built a toll-free bridge.

This sequence of events understandably had a dampening effect on non-government toll projects not only in Louisiana but elsewhere in the country, and such business practically vanished.

The Firm's very substantial success in founding Atlantic Aircraft Corporation, in 1920, was not quickly forgotten. Mr. Ford was particularly interested in this type of industrial development, in which the Firm used its own capital and thus was free to proceed solely on the basis of its own decisions.

Mr. Ford and others became intrigued with a plunger-cup patent for household washing machines. They saw that it represented a break-through in the "art" and could be incorporated into an appliance that would provide a superior result in home laundering, at the same time eliminating undue wear and tear on the textiles being washed.

FB&D acquired an interest in the patent, formed the Easy Washing Machine Company, designed and built a $1,000,000 plant in Syracuse, and managed the operation for several years before disposing of its holdings at a profit.

Next, the Firm put together the L. C. Smith and the Corona Typewriter companies, to form L. C. Smith and Corona Typewriters, Inc., with Mr. Ford as the first president of the merged company. Ford, Bacon & Davis managed the business for a number of years until deciding to sell its interest.

James F. Towers, later to be president and chairman of the Company, was active in this phase of the business and continued as a director of several of these sponsored companies long after Ford, Bacon & Davis had sold its interests in them.

Other enterprises were similarly developed for the Firm's own account, which turned out for the most part to be very profitable ventures, and certainly represented diversification. The Onondaga Silk Company of Syracuse made high fashion dress goods. The Prosperity Company places its optimistic name on laundry and pressing machines and equipment. Others included Allied Products Company of Detroit, a manufacturer of auto parts and dies, Teterboro Airport in New Jersey, and what is now Sealright Co., Inc., a subsidiary of Phillips Petroleum Company.

The United States in these years was consolidating its position as the world's leading industrial nation—a position which has never been challenged, either in volume or value.

Ever since the time the three-man partnership got its start in New Orleans, Ford, Bacon & Davis had been building a staff capable of handling not only engineering problems, but a number of closely-allied aspects of business as well. While internal promotions were a long-established tradition, capable men were frequently induced to come with the Company when their talents and experience were needed to strengthen some particular phase of operations, or to help handle a specific project. Men with outstanding reputations in their fields were usually happy to join an organization which was conceded to be a leader, in terms of professional prestige, and was certainly one of the largest and most active.

"Join Ford, Bacon & Davis and see the world from an upper berth" became a Company slogan, although no one ever rode in an upper berth if better space was available on the crowded trains. But travel was certainly the order of the day as staff engineers went in and out of the New York office on jobs involving their specialized know-how and experience.

This know-how by now covered every aspect of engineering—mechanical, civil, electrical and mining—and there were many outstanding men among them, internationally known for work on electric and steam railroads, industrial plants, power plants and pipelines, bridges and other structures, as well as valuation, depreciation, taxation and government regulation.

Based on experience, it was an article of faith among these men, physically tough and accustomed to working much of the time outdoors regardless of weather conditions, that assignments in Duluth inevitably came in the dead of winter, and those in Galveston just as the summer's worst heat wave got under way on the Gulf coast.

Then as now, the officers of the Company were always in close touch with every project, not alone through daily field reports but through site inspection at frequent intervals.

To handle a steadily-increasing volume of business, the staff had been expanding over the years, with emphasis on promising younger men who could be expected to assume major responsibility as the years went by.

With wide experience in selection of men, which had long been a key phase of its management work for clients, the Company during the latter years of the 1920's did extremely well for its own account.

In 1926, came Everett S. Coldwell, a graduate of MIT who was to become president 23 years later. Charles C. Whittelsey, who followed Mr. Coldwell as president, was hired in 1925.

Russell P. Westerhoff, graduate of MIT, joined the organization in 1928, to be elected president in 1965 when Mr. Whittelsey became chairman of the board.

It is typical of the Firm's policies that each of these men had a broad engineering background by the time he was selected to head the business, but each of them was also outstanding in a different area of the business. Mr. Coldwell was widely recognized as an industrial engineer and management consultant. Mr. Whittelsey, product of the Rolla School of Mines of the University of Missouri, has handled some of the important construction projects of modern times. Mr. Westerhoff, originally a specialist in hydraulics, had already compiled an impressive record in many phases of the business before his election as a vice-president in 1951.

About the time these men were coming into the organization, the Company in 1928 moved its main office in New York from 115 Broadway to larger quarters at 39 Broadway, where it remained for over 30 years. Some of the early years in these offices were to be gloomy ones, and not alone because of the long depression which struck in the 1930's. Mr. Ford died late in 1930, the first of the founders to go. Mr. Davis retired in 1928, but remained as a director through the hard years ahead. Mr. Bacon, who had been elected Chairman in 1928, was to continue in that position for nearly 20 more years.

The initial 1929 collapse of inflated security prices in itself was obviously an inevitable corrective development, and for some time it was generally regarded as such. Not for months did it become apparent that the stock market crash was the harbinger of drastic deflation and a prolonged business depression, to be accompanied by a major political upheaval.

Like others heavily dependent on industrial expansion for a large part of its business, Ford, Bacon & Davis was seriously affected by the dearth of engineering work of any kind as the depression deepened. But the organization, already some 35 years old, was determined to carry on.

In 1930 came a major assignment from the West Virginia Hydro-Electric Company, later to become part of the Electro Metallurgical Division of Union Carbide. This job called for the design and construction of a coal-fired steam power station with two 30,000 kw generating units at Boncar (Alloy) W.Va. The $3,100,000 job came in at minimum cost, compared with similar projects built around that time, and proved highly economical in production of power.

It was probably the first of the so-called mine-site power plants, and coal for its huge boilers came down by a cable conveyor system from an adjacent mountain-side mining operation.

An outstanding result on this initial construction work for Union Carbide helped further cement a long and mutually-profitable relationship, in which Ford, Bacon & Davis has designed and built over the years a number of important facilities for this company, one of the big three in the chemical industry of the world. Several of these projects required advanced engineering and technology, in which entirely new concepts were evolved and succesfully applied.

Even for major companies such as Union Carbide, construction jobs were soon to become few and far between, and many engineering organizations whose work was concentrated in that area were to fall by the wayside in the course of the long, harsh deflation that, by the end of 1930, loomed ominously ahead.

[87]

1931–1940

V

U.S. Economy, Honed on Hard Times, Revives as War Sweeps Europe

T HE DECADE of the 1930's is not a cherished memory among those who lived through it, watching a long depression wash out dreams of a new era of wealth and ease.

It was a brutal process, but from it emerged a lean and hungry industrial machine, fully competitive with the world's low cost producers and hardened for the challenge of war that lay ahead.

In retrospect, it seems probable that the depression had run its normal course by mid-1932, with the purchasing power of the dollar at a high level and most of the fat accumulated in the boom years trimmed away from production costs. Wages and salaries had been cut, and cut again. Payrolls had been trimmed. Only able and reliable employees, by and large, remained at work . . . and by no means all of them.

Government unemployment figures recorded a rise in the number of jobless from 1,550,000 in 1929 to a peak of 12,830,-000 in 1933, and a concurrent drop in number of employed (other than on farms) from 37,180,000 to 28,670,000.

Practically every industry was affected. Production of cars and trucks was a dramatic example, with unit volume down from a record 3,413,148 in 1929 to 1,331,860 in 1933, the lowest since the war year of 1918. Factory value was down even more—from $3,400,000,000 in 1929 to slightly over $750,000,000, lowest level in 16 years.

Construction shrank to almost nothing, and with it engineering assignments of practically every type. Many engineering and construction firms closed down entirely for lack of anything to do. Ford, Bacon & Davis was hard hit, forced to cut salaries and reduce the staff.

"It would have been easier to shrink way down, go fishing and in the end have more cash to show for it," said Mr. Bacon. "But less of a business."

By 1933, probably because of the uncertainties stemming from a change in the administration of the Federal Government, the banks of the nation had been closed and business was at a virtual standstill. Various artificial stimulants were applied to an almost moribund economy, including devaluation of the currency and abrogation of the gold standard except for settling international balances.

Nothing really worked until later in the decade, when the prospect, then the fact, of war in Europe brought huge contracts to aircraft and other industries for the weapons needed to stave off the growing threat of a resurgent Germany.

It was a discouraging time, but Ford, Bacon & Davis refused to knuckle under. This stubborn attitude attracted attention. In early 1932, while the gloom of the depression darkened the business horizon, a member of the editorial staff of the old American Magazine, seeking an interview, called on Mr. Bacon, who had taken over as chairman in 1928. The magazine was interested in a business philosophy that had weathered the storm so far, and seemed determined to "see it through."

Mr. Bacon was, among other things, highly articulate. As a result, in the May, 1932 issue of the magazine, appeared an article by Beverly Smith titled "When the Barriers Go Up, Who'll Be Out in Front?"

"One of the world's foremost industrial engineers," the article noted, "Mr. Bacon is not interested in publicity. Even during the war, when for a time he directed purchases for the Allies, very few beyond those with whom he did business ever heard his name.

"George Bacon's experience," a banker was quoted as saying, "has given him the clearest bird's-eye view of American industry of any man in the country. What's more, he's a highly intelligent bird.

"Mr. Bacon," the article went on, "is a man of medium height, slenderly built. He is 63 and looks all of 45. His brown hair is untinged with gray, and his keen, sunburned face is almost unlined. His weight, 140, is exactly what it was when he ran the ends for Cornell in the '90's. At 40 he took up tennis, and ever since has averaged about 80 games a week throughout the year.

"Engineers have long since traveled beyond the old dictionary definition of an engineer as 'one who manages engines.' Mr. Bacon, I suppose, has traveled farther than most of them. Working today on plans for carrying a high pressure pipe line across a thousand miles of river, swamp and mountain, he may have to turn his mind tomorrow to studying production methods in the salmon fisheries of British Columbia. Settling a feud in the directorate of an ailing corporation or advising a foreign government how to balance its budget may all be in the day's work for him.

"As chairman of the board of Ford, Bacon & Davis, Inc., he directs the most diversified, and probably the largest independently-owned engineering organization in the world. We might call him a surgeon of industry.

"From his New York office, with its staff of more than 200 engineers, experts in most phases of industry, he supervises economic and business studies, design of plants and equipment, construction, operation, management and appraisal, all over the United States and in half a dozen foreign lands.

"His men are trained to tackle any business problem, however large, small, romantic or bizarre—whether it be building street railways in Portugal, finding a cheaper way to put tops on milk bottles, evaluating a $200,000,000 oil company, reorganizing a Santo Domingo banana plantation, investigating a new television invention, or pointing out better distribution methods to a wholesale bee raiser.

"He is as calm a man as I ever have seen. Whether in his spacious, walnut-lined New York office overlooking the Hudson River, besieged by phone calls and telegrams, or in his old-fashioned studio apartment, he is utterly relaxed. He does not twiddle with a pencil, nor cover a piece of paper with diagrams. He seems at ease with himself and the world.

"We sat in comfortable chairs before an open fire in his library as he gave me a glimpse of his 'bird's-eye' view of industry:

"I am not going to try to minimize the business depression. Everybody knows how credit has frozen, how consumption and employment and production have slowed up. But everybody seems to have forgotten that there is no depression whatever in the progress of human knowledge. Inventive genius is not frozen. Improvements in methods of production, in engineering efficiency, in merchandising practice, in economics of distribution—these have not slowed up.

"They are going forward faster than ever . . . and the men who realize this will be the leaders when the inevitable upturn comes. The men who sit around paralyzed with fright, mourning the 'good old days' of 1928 and 1929—they will be in the ruck.

"The truth is that the golden boom days were, in one sense, a time of stagnation. Everybody was too much obsessed with volume production to worry about mere efficiency. Sales were mushrooming every day. There was no time to pause for improvements of method, for reorganization of management and personnel. Volume, and yet more volume, was the watchword.

"Today, all this is changed. Plants stand idle or run on part time. This is the ideal time for the wide-awake businessman to bring his plant, his business methods within and without his plant, down to earth and up to the standard the competitive pace the future will require.

"This is not a time for despair. It's a time for opportunity. The successful men of the future will be those who now realize that much of the glittering volume-producing machinery of three years ago will be obsolescent by 1935.

"Change is the law of life. It is the keynote of business. Business exists to give people what they want. Their wants are in a constant state of flux. Change goes far faster than men can know.

"Our first big jobs were electrifying horse car lines. Today, they're tearing up the tracks. We laid pipe lines in 1915. They were primitive compared with the pipe lines we laid in 1925. Yet our methods of 1925 were out of date in 1928.

"Today particularly is a time of opportunity for young men. Three years ago it seemed that all the problems had been solved . . . all the battles won. The industrial engine, apparently, was perfect, and the men at the top had all the power and knew all the secrets. For the young man, there was soft comfort and insipid luxury ahead—no struggle, no excitement, no achievement.

EDGAR G. HILL
Director, 1930–1948
A founder and first president (1931–1948) of
Ford, Bacon & Davis Construction Company

"That too has changed. The board has been swept rather clean. Men and industries have been brought back to scratch. A new race, a new battle looms. Don't think there's anything soft about it. Young men will have to learn something about the plain living and hard thinking their daddies used to know. Perhaps a third of our present industrial plant will have to be junked . . . written off . . . forgotten. Heaven knows that means pain and trouble. It has to be. The scrap heap and the ash barrel are going to claim an awful lot of our play-toys in the next two years, and don't forget it.

"Fortunes are not made in boom times. That is merely the collection period. They are really made in times of adversity. Then the wise, strong man, young or old, overhauls his mind, gets in training for the race that is to come."

In line with the philosophy expounded by Mr. Bacon, that depressions provide opportunity, Ford, Bacon & Davis chose March, 1931, as a suitable time to form Ford, Bacon & Davis Construction Corporation, a wholly-owned subsidiary with headquarters in Monroe, La. It was Edgar G. Hill who sponsored the idea of a separate corporate entity to handle this important phase of the business. He became its first president, and served as its chief executive until his retirement in 1948, after 28 years of service.

Although much construction was handled on a fee basis, it was sometimes necessary to engage in competitive bidding. Under adverse circumstances, impossible to foresee, this could subject the entire organization to unnecessary risk. A separate corporation, wholly-owned, adequately capitalized and having full access to the technical resources of the parent organization, could undertake risks that would otherwise be imprudent.

Offices and other facilities were established in Monroe, La., where the firm had maintained job headquarters in much previous work in the Gulf area, and where further growth, even though it was to be some years away, was clearly apparent. Louisiana, including known reserves offshore in the Gulf of Mexico, represents one of the world's major deposits of natural gas and major discoveries are still being made. Gulf Oil, for example, in 1964 brought in a well on acreage jointly owned with Humble, which has a calculated open-flow potential of a fantastic 650 million cubic feet daily.

The decade of the 1930's was by no means as sterile and stagnant as depression made it seem at the time. Under the grinding pressure of a vicious cost-price squeeze, industry was fast developing more efficient, more economical production methods.

The year 1934 was marked by an announcement which, at the time, attracted scant attention, probably because its significance was not widely understood. The Nobel prize in chemistry was awarded to Harold Clayton Urey "for his discovery of heavy hydrogen," which had attracted still less attention when it was made in 1931.

This was the break-through that provided the basis for the development in later years of atomic energy, harnessed first for destruction but now coming into use as a source of electric power, and one which, unlike the fossil fuels, is inexhaustible.

The development of nylon was under way, and both fibres and yarn were marketed by 1939. Edwin H. Armstrong, genius of radio, invented FM (frequency modulation, static free) in 1939. The sulfa drugs proved successful against many diseases.

Such advances as synthetic abrasives, hydraulic feed, pneumatic accessories, electric drive and control, led to the redesign of vastly more efficient machine tools. Growth industries such as petroleum chemicals and electrical equipment characteristically continued to expand, if more slowly.

Installed electric generating capacity continued to rise in the early years of the depression. From the 1929 peak of 38,708,000

KW, it moved to 43,000,000 in 1933, then levelled off until 1936, when it rose to 43,582,000 and continued upward to nearly 51,000,000 as the decade ended in 1940.

Use of electric power was similarly resistant to the sharp decline in general business, and from the record high of 1929 at 117,914 million kilowatt hours, slid to a low of 100,353 million kwh in 1932, then climbed sharply to 181,706 million kwh by 1940.

The telephone industry, too, adjusted to the slump, but stations in service fell from a peak of 20,202,000 in 1930 to a low of 16,711,000 in 1933, before recovering to end the decade with nearly 22,000,000 in service. This was equal to 165.0 per 1,000 population, topping the previous high of 163.8 per 1,000 in 1929.

Highway traffic, which reached nearly 198 billion vehicle miles in 1929, continued to grow and in 1931 totalled 216 billion. In 1932 and 1933, it dropped to 200 billion and then resumed the steady uptrend which had been under way for over 20 years. By 1940, total truck, bus and car mileage was estimated at 302 billion miles, a figure which would be doubled in the next 15 years.

Both petroleum and natural gas, basically growth industries in the true sense of the term, proved relatively stable, although prices were off sharply. Petroleum output, which dropped from a billion barrels in 1929 to 785,000,000 barrels in 1932, was back to 1,100,000,000 barrels by 1936 and heading toward 1,353,000,-000 barrels by 1940, more than a third above the 1929 peak.

Natural gas production, which reached 1,979 billion cubic feet at its 1930 peak, dropped to less than 1.6 billion cubic feet in 1932 and 1933, but by 1940 was up to 2,734 billion cubic feet, also more than a third above the 1929 level. The price had dropped from 8.2 cents per thousand cubic feet in 1929, to 4.5 cents per thousand cubic feet.

Steel production, which collapsed from its all-time high of 56,400,000 tons in 1929 to only 13,700,000 tons in 1932, was close to 60,000,000 tons by 1940, as war in Europe flooded the industry with urgent orders.

Fortunately, in view of the war which loomed not far ahead, the installed capacity of the steel industry was maintained at high levels through the depression years, and in fact rose from its previous peak of 71,000,000 tons in 1930 to 81,000,000 tons in 1940.

The steady, long-term advance in U.S. productive efficiency continued through the depression years. The index of output per man-hour (1929 equals 100) rose to 124 in 1940, compared with 97.5 in 1930. (In 1894, when FB&D was founded, it had been 49.5).

As Mr. Bacon had said, creative forces were not affected by depression. Within a short time after construction, in the mid-'20's, of the Interstate Pipe Line which ran through some miles of swampland in Louisiana, severe corrosion was discovered. The problem was serious and demanded a solution. A laboratory was set up in the offices at 39 Broadway, soil and water samples were brought in from various areas and the behavior of pipe was tested and studied under various simulated conditions.

This intensive research eventually led to the invention and patenting of the Ford, Bacon & Davis Cathodic Protection Method, which uses multiple anodes acting to decrease or even reverse the flow of electric current from pipe to soil, thus retarding or stopping corrosion. This was the inception of a whole new technology in prevention of this type of corrosion, and the basic cathodic principle is widely used today in a broad range of applications, including ship and boat hulls.

As a separate but related study, examinations were made of pipe in underground service. A marked slow-down of pit penetration over a period of time was discovered. Pit depths were tabulated and analyzed, and demonstrable relationships found between depth of pitting and the physical condition of the pipe. The studies proved extremely valuable as a factor in determining depreciation of pipe in connection with valuations of property in rate cases.

The dearth of normal engineering work and the almost complete cessation of construction activity stimulated an active search by the organization for opportunities in which engineering and production know-how could be profitably employed. New legislation in the early 1930's was a favorable factor.

Repeal of Prohibition in 1933 led almost immediately to a total of 66 assignments to Ford, Bacon & Davis in connection with the re-establishment of the brewing and distilling industries, involving surveys, appraisals and reports, as well as design and construction of new facilities.

Beer came back first, and for all practical purposes a new industry had to be created overnight, and on a large scale. Only a very few breweries had survived on what was known as "near beer," a non-alcoholic brew which never gained wide acceptance. This meant feasibility studies, data for financing, design and construction of facilities and market evaluations.

Few men were still active who had known the business in pre-Prohibition days, but the Ford, Bacon & Davis files contained a wealth of information on old brewery jobs which could be quickly brought up to date on costs, methods and other factors. Conferences were held with several prominent brewer-clients. Against this background a study was prepared on the economics of the industry which, distributed to a suitable mailing list, brought in work.

Late in 1933, when Prohibition was repealed, the same procedure proved equally successful in the distilling industry, and gave Ford, Bacon & Davis an important role in re-establishing this industry, shrunk to almost nothing so far as legal operations were concerned.

The Securities and Exchange Act of 1933 was another important factor in generating business during this period. Ford, Bacon & Davis men conferred with Securities and Exchange Commission members and prepared a series of papers on registration under the new law, outlining the liabilities which might be incurred and methods of obtaining relief from such legal hazards. For several years, as a result, Ford, Bacon & Davis was involved in investigations and reports for underwriters and others concerned with new securities offerings.

The 1930's were a time of trouble for the power utilities, even though their business proved relatively stable during the long deflation. This, together with a continuing flow of assignments for rate-making valuations, was another source of much-needed business during the decade.

Clients involved in rate cases at this time included Cities Service subsidiaries in Arkansas and Louisiana; East Ohio Gas Company; Puget Sound Power & Light Company of Seattle; subsidiaries of Columbia Engineering & Management Corp., now the Columbia Gas System; and the Appalachian Electric Power Company and Wheeling Electric Company, subsidiaries of American Gas & Electric Company, now American Power Company.

Trouble other than rate cases was implicit in the assignment to Ford, Bacon & Davis by Alabama Power Company, in 1934, of an appraisal and determination of severance damages on property the Tennessee Valley Authority sought to acquire.

One of the major casualties of the times was the huge Associated Gas & Electric Company. Under the Public Utility Holding Company Act, Associated was, like other non-integrated systems, required to register and then to break up into independent regional units. Beginning in 1935, Ford, Bacon & Davis made valuations of the numerous Associated subsidiaries. It was a large and complex undertaking, involving properties with a total value, as finally appraised, of something over $500,000,000. From an operating standpoint, Associated, like many of the big holding companies, was an extremely well-managed system and a low-cost supplier of power in its territories. The trouble lay rather in the over-capitalization which had taken place as operating properties were pyramided into holding companies, and then in some cases, holding companies were grouped into super-holding companies.

Along with the pick-up in business during the mid-30's came the need for additional staff. Lionel S. Baldin, a graduate of Columbia University, and later to become a vice president specializing in valuations and reports, joined the organization in mid-1935 after several years of experience in accounting and utility work, as well as in research and teaching.

The following year, Thomas I. Crowell, Jr., graduate of Yale University, was hired, later to be a director and vice president in charge of report work. It was he who collected and organized the material on which this history is largely based.

In 1935 the FB&D organization was retained to study and report on various problems connected with the installation of a continuous strip mill at the Gary Works of the American Sheet and Tin Plate Company, a subsidiary of the United States Steel Corporation. Following this came a similar assignment on Universal Atlas Cement, another U.S. Steel subsidiary.

The results were apparently satisfactory to management, since shortly after they were completed, Ford, Bacon & Davis was retained to make a complete and thorough study of the entire corporation, covering all its subsidiaries and all phases of its operations.

As it happened, two of the Ford, Bacon & Davis men assigned to the work were named Jones and Laughlin, and their frequent visits to the U.S. Steel headquarters at 71 Broadway soon led to the comment that "things have come to a pretty pass when we have to get Jones and Laughlin in to show us how to run the business."

It was a mammoth job, still one of the largest of its kind ever undertaken and the basis for many of the management decisions which have since strengthened the Corporation's competitive position in its industry.

The study, actually a series of studies, covered the organization, operations, facilities, markets and potential markets of the entire corporation. A number of other consulting firms, in such specialized fields as accounting and finance, were retained by Ford, Bacon & Davis in connection with the huge project.

A total of over 200 reports was the end result, when the job was completed in 1938.

The slow, irregular recovery in general business which had begun in 1932 continued, with minor set-backs, into 1937. Then, late in the year, a swift decline set in which carried into 1938. Again, valuation and rate work stood Ford, Bacon & Davis in good stead, and important revaluations were made during this period for East Ohio Gas Company, The People's Natural Gas Company, Hope Natural Gas Company and New York State Natural Gas Corporation.

This work had been primarily to estimate the current fair value of the properties, based largely on reproduction cost and trended original cost, for use in determining rate bases.

About that time, on June 21, 1938, the Natural Gas Act became law, with far-reaching effects on the industry when, in the famous Hope case, more than five years later, the Supreme Court held that under the Act, a finding of the "fair value of the property" was not necessary in establishing "just and reasonable" rates.

Work not connected with the war gained in volume during the latter years of the decade. One of the more important projects came in 1940, when American Smelting & Refining Company required an appraisal of its extensive properties in Mexico. This included silver and other mines in remote areas, often at high altitudes, and provided travel experiences and new scenery for the staff assigned to the job.

A few industries grew rapidly through the 1930's, among them the airlines. Passenger miles on scheduled domestic lines rose from 85,125,000 in 1930 to over a billion in 1940. In 1938, Ford, Bacon & Davis was retained by United Airlines to make a long-range study of potential markets for airline passenger traffic, as a basis for planning future needs in terms of equipment, terminal facilities and organization.

The decade ended with business activity moving sharply upward as huge contracts for arms and supplies forced industry to expand. In 1940, Ford, Bacon & Davis started working on a series of large design and construction projects for Union Carbide. A new chemical plant at Texas City, Tex., got under way later in the year, based on use of gases from oil refinery operations in the area. The initial cost was around $10,000,000, but so successful did the concept prove that $120,000,000 was eventually invested in the huge facility, under designs prepared by company engineers. Ford, Bacon & Davis handled this later construction as well.

Toward the end of the decade, work was also started on a new generating unit at Union Carbide's Electro Metallurgical Division plant in Alloy, West Va., to add some 40,000 kw of capacity to the steam power station which Ford, Bacon & Davis had originally built back in 1930.

It was in 1940 that Ford, Bacon & Davis was first retained by Jacobs Aircraft Engine Company to take over management of the company and supervise all operations, in order to complete a contract from the Canadian Government which called for delivery of 1,500 engines a month for new P-60 trainer planes. The company's Pottstown plant was expanded and production stepped up rapidly.

These crash assignments, as events would soon prove, were only a foretaste of the hectic pace and crushing pressures under which Ford, Bacon & Davis men would work for the next four years and more. As the decade came to an end, American industry was "warming up" for a performance which, in terms of quantity, value and variety of production, had not been seen before in history.

It was to be an achievement of industrial and engineering ability and know-how that was believable only when it became an accomplished fact.

1941–1950

VI

Industrial Output Overwhelms
Enemies Across Two Oceans

THE UNITED STATES by 1941 was moving swiftly and surely toward full participation in a war that had been smoldering in Europe since the Russo-German invasion of Poland in September, 1939. Industry was operating at capacity and rushing to build the new plants needed to strengthen a desperate European alliance, cracking before the German onslaught.

France had fallen in mid-1940, and the Reich stretched from Calais to the Russian border, which German troops and tanks crossed in June, 1941, on their way to Stalingrad.

Americans had been engaged in all-out war on the industrial front long before the historic Sunday morning bombing of Pearl Harbor on December 7, 1941.

Steel production shot up from 28,000,000 tons in 1939, when Hitler invaded Austria, to an all-time high of close to 60,000,000 tons in 1940. Electric power output rose sharply in the same period to a record 180 billion kilowatt hours from 142 billion in

1938. Production of primary aluminum more than doubled from 143,000 tons to 309,000 tons in 1941.

Aircraft production, which totalled less than $200,000,000 in value in 1938, rose to $370,000,000 in 1940, a drop in the bucket compared with what happened in this key industry in the next few years. Incredibly, the U.S. aircraft industry in the five years 1941–1945 was to build over 305,000 bombers, transports, fighters and trainers valued at over $44 billion.

It was undoubtedly the most spectacular single example of an industrial performance that, in a period of 45 months, crushed two powerful enemies who had been gearing themselves for all-out war for nearly a decade—and in both cases, brought this overwhelming power to bear at the enemy's doorstep, thousands of miles away from the factories that produced it, a fact often overlooked in measuring the immensity of the achievement.

For Ford, Bacon & Davis, these were busy years. An unprecedented challenge lay ahead—to help create the plants and facilities which could support a war machine operating on two fronts, each of them an ocean away from its base of supply.

Defense work in ever-increasing volume continued to pour in through 1941. For the Defense Plant Corporation, the firm was commissioned to design and construct a huge, entirely new plant for Jacobs Aircraft Engine Company, now a subsidiary of Allied Aero Industries, Inc. The new facility, the latest thing in "blackout" design, had no windows and was completely air-conditioned. With about 8,000 employees, it produced under license, a 450-hp Pratt & Whitney engine. The operation was under the direction of Cornelius J. Abbott, a graduate of Case Institute of Applied Science at Cleveland, who, representing FB&D, acted as president of Jacobs. The company continued under FB&D management after completion of the construction, which involved a total of about $18,000,000.

While this was going on, FB&D also undertook for Busch-Sulzer Brothers Diesel Engine Company, organized by the St.

Louis brewing family, the design and supervision of construction of a plant to make powder and projectile hoists for the U.S. Navy. This equipment was used to move ammunition from magazines to the 5-inch anti-aircraft guns which were installed on merchant ships, as well as Navy vessels, during the war.

War accelerated a major pipeline project in 1941, which was conceived to eliminate the risk of tanker shipments out of New Orleans to supply the Southeastern states. The idea had been conceived and was under study by Ford, Bacon & Davis in connection with plans for more economical and efficient distribution from the big Standard Oil of New Jersey refinery at Baton Rouge, under normal economic conditions. Under war conditions, and with the vulnerability of tankers to submarine attack, the need for the pipeline immediately became urgent.

Using plans and engineering surveys already made by the Firm, the work got under way in 1941, under FB&D supervision. This was the Plantation Pipe Line, which runs 1,267 miles from Louisiana to Greensboro, N.C., and is owned by Standard Oil of Kentucky and Shell Oil, as well as New Jersey Standard.

A similar situation existed farther north. A glance at the map indicates the shorter land distance between Portland, Me. and Montreal, as compared with the water route via the St. Lawrence River. Ford, Bacon & Davis worked closely with Standard of New Jersey in preliminary work on this project. The original pipe line was built in the late 1930's. In 1941, FB&D designed and supervised construction of the big oil terminal required at Portland to supply the new line. The project saved many miles on tanker trips from Venezuela and Gulf ports, and provided Montreal with a year-round supply of petroleum products, previously cut off by winter freezing of the river. This eliminated the cost of maintaining large storage facilities and inventories near the city.

One of the early Government defense projects involved, for those assigned to it, a stay in Bermuda, where a U.S. Army Air

Base was under construction. This was a $33,000,000 project, later known as Fort Bell and Kindley Field, in which two other firms were participants as architects and engineers. This shared responsibility helped make available the manpower to bring the job to early completion—a primary consideration in all defense work, then and later.

The biggest and one of the most important projects assigned to FB&D in 1941, as the nation mobilized for the all-out war that appeared to be inevitable, was the design, construction and operation of a $25,000,000 Army Ordnance facility at Jacksonville, Ark., known as the Arkansas Ordnance Plant.

FB&D provided the initial architect-engineer services in connection with the plant, then supervised its construction, which involved some unusual features for safe handling of the hypersensitive explosives used in detonators, boosters, fuses and primers. As contractors for construction, FB&D at the peak employed over 13,000 carpenters, plumbers, electricians, riggers and other craftsmen in pushing the work to completion.

Labor unions were unable to supply adequate manpower in that area, and the job was completed on an open-shop basis, with a great deal of on-the-job training. Superior workers also had to be selected and trained to provide supervision as foremen.

Despite the tight supply of craftsmen and laborers, the job was completed in line with an extremely tight schedule, some of the construction personnel being retained as operations got under way. Under Ford, Bacon & Davis management, the plant at the peak employed some 14,000.

Although for the most part inexperienced as industrial workers, the people who swarmed in to man the Jacksonville plant proved eager to learn and soon did. During the next 42 months, the plant was awarded the Army-Navy "E" for excellence four times for its performance in meeting production quotas.

As this would indicate, these men and women were basically intelligent and more than made up for lack of training or experience by intense patriotism and a determination to do whatever was required of them. They were, many of them, also quick-witted and shrewd. One man, picked up for an infraction of some plant rule by a guard, thought fast. Asked for his badge number as the guard wrote out a "ticket," he read off the number on the guard's badge, with the result that it was the guard who was later summoned for reprimand. This is, of course, an ancient device in the art of flouting authority, but it takes a good man to think of it in time.

At the peak, there were some 35,000 people on Ford, Bacon & Davis payrolls, in the main office in New York, at construction sites, and in completed plants that were under FB&D management, or in the case of top engineering personnel, traveling from one to the other by plane, train, bus or car.

It was a hectic time, in which physical stamina and a sense of humor were probably the two most important ingredients for survival. Since modern war is basically an engineering problem—in the production and movement of material, and the supply of troops—experienced engineers were in desperately short supply relative to the work that demanded their skills.

As a result, men were working 16 and 20-hour days, six or seven days a week for months on end, and under heavy pressure in the knowledge that human lives depended on scheduled completion of the projects for which they were responsible.

Ford, Bacon & Davis, like others stretched to the breaking point, was finally forced to limit the amount of new work and responsibility it could assume in order to give its hard-pressed staff a fair chance to complete the work already under way.

That the organization got through the long grind without casualties among its key people, and without costly confusion and delay on any project entrusted to it, was a tribute to management experience acquired over the years. It was this long experience that made possible the effective allocation of special talent and ability in the right place, at the right time, and in the precise amount required to get the job done.

To handle as much as possible of the work which deluged the

organization, the staff was drastically enlarged and additional space taken in buildings near the New York office.

The office space problem was further complicated by the fact that large sections were, by Government edict, under Security Regulations, which meant that only employees with appropriate security clearance could enter. Much work was in so-called "sensitive" areas. This became especially important when certain very large engineering activities got under way in an unlikely small Tennessee community later known to the world as Oak Ridge.

As Government assignments assumed increasing, in fact overwhelming, preponderance in the firm's business, a Washington "headquarters" became essential. A room, No. 710, was leased at the Carlton Hotel, which provided overnight accommodations as needed. Space in the city was so scarce, however, that the hotel insisted under the terms of the lease, that the room be rented to others if not occupied. On many nights, an engineer from the New York office would arrive late in Washington for an early appointment on the following day. Some sleepy occupant would have to get up and move to a basement dormitory which the hotel operated to accommodate desperate travelers.

Not only was the firm working on a round-the-clock basis, with most of the professional staff carrying responsibilities that normally would require at least two men, but supplying talent to Government agencies as well.

When the Defense Plant Corporation was organized by the RFC to handle a crash program to expand war production facilities, there was an immediate need for an engineering department which could deal knowledgeably with the contractors, architects and others commissioned to handle DPC projects. Industrial plant construction by the Government reached a peak of over $3.4 billion in 1942, on top of private industrial construction totalling $340,000,000.

As a result, Harry E. Whitaker was placed on temporary leave with RFC to supervise the organization "from scratch" of an engineering department which would supervise this gigantic Government program. He not only survived the ordeal but carried out the job in such a way as to earn high commendation from all concerned. Mr. Whitaker, who had been chief engineer of FB&D since 1937, was elected a director in 1941, and on his return from the Government assignment in 1944, was elected vice-president and chief engineer.

Ford, Bacon & Davis during this period was also a principal consultant to the RFC and the Army Corps of Engineers in establishing a standard scale of fees for architects, engineers and constructors who participated in this massive program, without question the largest undertaking of its kind in history.

While these huge defense projects were necessarily handled on a "cost-plus" basis, they nonetheless involved real and very substantial risk to the contractors involved since reimbursement for money spent was subject to scrutiny under the rules and regulations that surround Government operations. With millions of dollars involved, questions always hung in the air—who would pay for mishaps or catastrophes?

It was a difficult, ever-present problem and required painstaking care from the time the contract was negotiated and written to the final audit, with scrupulous attention to every detail all through the construction period.

And if this were not enough strain on the nerves of the responsible engineers, in the case of the $25,000,000 Arkansas Ordnance facility there was the added problem of devising and establishing operating techniques for a completely new, and to say the least hazardous process—making and loading 1,000,000 detonators a day with the two most sensitive explosives known to man—fulminate and lead azide.

At this plant too, Ford, Bacon & Davis became involved in an intra-agency conflict that could have had serious repercussions. The Army's commanding officer at the plant ordered overtime, with no premium to be paid to employees over their straight time rate. Another agency claiming jurisdiction ordered that premium rates must be paid for all overtime.

Hoping for the best, Ford, Bacon & Davis reviewed the contract, followed the orders of the commanding officer, and was promptly sued by a group of employees who claimed overtime wages. Army attorneys rallied to defend Ford, Bacon & Davis. Other Government attorneys intervened on behalf of the employees. The dispute was finally decided in favor of Ford, Bacon & Davis, acting under the orders of the commanding officer. While it was pending, of course, the litigation made no contribution to the peace of mind of those involved, pushed as they were to the outer limits of endurance by far more urgent responsibilities.

The problem of disallowance of expenses was no empty threat. A contractor building a TNT plant near St. Louis was unable to get labor at the site, since there was no available public transportation. Simply to get the job completed according to his contract, he was forced to spend $100,000 to establish his own bus transportation to the plant. It came out of his own pocket, since his expense claim was disallowed.

In addition to its work in Arkansas, the Firm in 1942–1943 was assigned to design and build the $21,400,000 Longhorn Ordnance Plant at Karnack, Tex., for the Army, with Edgar G. Hill in charge. This facility produced TNT for use in artillery and mortar projectiles and bombs, under the management of Monsanto Chemical Company.

With these heavy involvements continuing, the Firm was also acting as consultant on the design, construction and operation of three other big ordnance facilities—the Vigo Ordnance Plant at Terre Haute, Ind., the Sangamon Ordnance Plant at Springfield, Ill., and the Scioto Ordnance Plant at Marion, Ohio. Continental Can Company operated the Terre Haute facility; Remington Rand the plant at Springfield, and United States

Rubber the Marion installation. Each of the three cost about $24,000,000.

While this was going on, another Ford, Bacon & Davis team was involved in designing and constructing, during 1941, a major power plant expansion and improvement project at the Naval Torpedo Station and Training Station in Newport, R.I.

Following Pearl Harbor, at the close of 1941, of course, this breakneck pace was no longer adequate, and had to be stepped up sharply. The engineering and construction staff was further enlarged to the extent that competent personnel could be found, and operations went on a grueling round the clock schedule with everyone working to the limit of his physical capacity—which many discovered to be considerably greater than they had ever suspected. Although by the time it was over nobody felt he could or would ever want to try it again.

It was early in 1942 that James F. Towers, elected executive vice-president in 1941, took over from Mr. von Phul, who had served as president since 1921. Mr. Towers headed the company as president through the war years. He also became chairman when Mr. Bacon, last of the founding partners active in the business, retired in 1946, and continued as chairman and president until his own retirement in 1949.

In 1942, one of the first emergency demands came from the Navy, which needed additional facilities for building submarines. Ford, Bacon & Davis was assigned to rehabilitate and expand, for this purpose, the old Groton Iron Works shipyard at Groton, Conn., close to the big Electric Boat Co. yards.

The facility, which had been idle for some years, had originally built various small craft. The rebuilt and vastly expanded plant and yards were put in service in record time, renamed "Victory Yard," and turned over to Electric Boat, which operated them through the rest of the war. Electric Boat, founded in 1899, was the nucleus around which the late John Jay Hopkins,

JAMES F. TOWERS
Director, 1929–1949
President, 1942–1949
Chairman, 1946–1949

who became president in 1947, put together today's General Dynamics Corporation. It was and is unique as the world's only non-government enterprise devoted to the design and construction of submarines, and traces its corporate ancestry back to the early development of this powerful naval weapon.

Along with its own Government work, Ford, Bacon & Davis undertook some very large projects for clients who were acting as agents for the Defense Plant Corporation.

One of those was a tin smelter at Texas City, Tex. Most of the world's tin supply had been refined in England and Holland, and the supply was vulnerable to enemy action. Accordingly, a plan was made to eliminate this risk by building facilities in the United States. The operation was assigned to the Tin Processing Corporation. This was a subsidiary set up by the Billiton Company, a Dutch corporation with wide experience in the mining and smelting of this critical material, essential in canning and other industries. Design and construction of the $6,300,000 plant was assigned to Ford, Bacon & Davis.

Similarly, the United States economy was dependent on large imports of natural rubber from the Dutch East Indies and other remote areas which could be cut off by enemy action. Accordingly, a crash program was set up to replace this essential rubber latex with a synthetic product.

For the account of the Defense Plant Corporation, through Union Carbide, Ford, Bacon & Davis took over the design, other than process, and the construction of butadiene and styrene plants at Institute, West Va., in 1941–1942. The Firm also handled design and construction of adjacent buildings and utilities for a copolymer plant. The three huge facilities comprised the world's largest integrated complex for production of so-called Buna S rubber. The butadiene and styrene plants operated by Union Carbide were built under the supervision of Mr. Whittelsey at a cost of $45,000,000. Construction was started on the first butadiene plant in April, 1942, and the initial unit

A key segment of the synthetic rubber program which saved the U.S. from a disastrous shortage in World War II, the copolymer plant above was built in part by FB&D at Institute, West Va., for operation by U.S. Rubber Company, now Uniroyal.

Carbon & Carbide Chemicals Corp., subsidiary of Union Carbide, was the operator of the butadiene and styrene plant designed and built at Institute, West Va., as part of the crash program to meet synthetic rubber needs in the early 1940's.

was in production January 28, 1943, two months ahead of schedule.

The project involved the closing of the Charleston airport, but a device was rigged by the construction crews so that there was daily delivery and pickup of air mail with the cooperation of the Post Office Department. Working with Mr. Whittelsey on the projects were Russell P. Westerhoff, assistant project manager, George O. Phillips, a graduate of Louisiana Polytechnic Institute, as general superintendent, and W. A. White, a graduate of Brown University, as project engineer.

Concurrently with this outstanding performance, Ford, Bacon & Davis was assigned the job of design and construction for a butadiene plant at Louisville, Ky., a $33,500,000 job which also came in ahead of schedule.

Thus the firm brought to completion in a period of months, about $100,000,000 of engineering and construction work to provide the nation with its essential supplies of tin and rubber for war. It was a spectacular performance, largely made possible by close teamwork and intensive effort on the part of the workers and the engineers and supervisory personnel involved.

Large quantities of grain alcohol were consumed by these synthetic rubber plants. The alcohol was transported in tank cars which were promptly emptied into the plant storage facilities on arrival. Vapor remained, however, and in the cool nights would condense into appreciable quantities of 180–190 proof alcohol in the bottom of the car. This, for drinking purposes, was a potent beverage, as some of the workmen at the plants very soon discovered. Guards were only partially successful in blocking off this welcome, if unusual, supply of spirits from thirsty employees, despite the gigantic hangovers it generated.

Carbon black, largely obtained by incomplete cumbustion of natural gas, is essential in the manufacture of tires and other rubber products and was needed in large volume as synthetic rubber came into production.

United Carbon Co., an important producer, was an old client for whom Ford, Bacon & Davis had worked in past years. Appointed agent of the Defense Plant Corporation to obtain additional supplies of this ingredient, the company turned to FB&D for the design and construction of an $18,900,000 plant in Odessa, Tex., close to plentiful supplies of natural gas.

Another large project, in which Harrisburg Steel Corporation was agent for the DPC, came in at about the same time, involving design and construction of a plant at Harrisburg for the production of aerial demolition bombs and high-pressure gas cylinders. This was an $8,130,000 project by the time it went into full production.

Both jobs, although part of an incredible work-load the organization was handling at the time, were completed on schedule and put into production without the delays often encountered in obtaining efficient performance from installations of this type, unprecedented in size and complexity.

In the years 1940–1942 alone, Ford, Bacon & Davis assumed major engineering responsibilities on more than 30 projects, military installations and industrial facilities, involving a total of over $330,000,000, and in many cases continued to operate the new plants for some time after they were completed.

One of the more important of the firm's wartime assignments involved no construction. Douglas Aircraft Corporation decided that outside consultants could help in setting up more effective production planning control in its great Santa Monica plant, which was operating around the clock, seven days a week.

Two FB&D men were sent out in the client's own DC-3, which was known as the NC-30,000. The type was a famous workhorse plane of its time and one of the superb designs that helped make Douglas big. At the end of their trip, the two FB&D men were aghast to find themselves coming down to land in what appeared to be a better residential section of Santa Monica.

They were reassured. It was camouflage. The entire plant,

which covered acres, and its adjacent landing field were disguised with carefully simulated houses, streets and trees so that it appeared to be part of the city itself. Recovering quickly from minor shock, the engineers proceeded to their assignment and completed it successfully. The huge plant was a major source of the overwhelming air power that helped defeat the Axis powers.

Numerous smaller jobs had to be handled along with the big ones, despite the effort to impose a limit to the strain under which the engineering staff, and for that matter every other part of the organization, was operating.

Acting for the Defense Plant Corporation, the Nicaro Nickel Company commissioned FB&D to handle preliminary studies on the engineering and design for plants to recover nickel near Preston, Cuba.

About the same time, the Puerto Rico legislature passed a law designating the so-called Sugar Centrals on the island as "public utilities," subject to regulation by the Public Utilities Commission.

Fajardo Sugar Company and Eastern Sugar Associates, two of the four largest sugar companies in Puerto Rico, engaged FB&D in 1943 to make valuations of their properties in anticipation of price-regulation. Early in the year a crew of 12 men under Peter Antonelli, a graduate of Cornell University, was selected and sent, not at all unwillingly, out to the island. In a much more benign climate than might otherwise have been their lot, they made valuations of seven of the sugar centrals. In 1944 and 1945, testimony was presented to the Utilities Commission on behalf of Fajardo.

The case, as it turned out, never reached a decision and eventually the law was repealed. Since the price of raw sugar was fixed in world markets, supplemented in Puerto Rico by certain controls under the U.S. Department of Agriculture, there was, in fact, nothing for the Public Utilities Commission to regulate. Coming during the peak of war activities, this strange assignment provided a sort of working vacation in a pleasant land for those delegated to do the job.

In addition to the hundreds of millions of dollars of design and construction work which Ford, Bacon & Davis handled during the 1940's, the organization also contributed valuable manpower to varied Government operations. In fact, James F. Towers, who became executive vice-president in February, 1941, served for a time as a dollar-a-year man with the War Production Board in Washington. David A. Uebelacker served with the WPB, with the Foreign Economic Administration in London, and also for a time with the Lend-Lease Administration. Mr. Uebelacker, a graduate of Princeton University, was later a vice-president and director, serving as manager of new business and as representative of the Firm in Canada for some years before his retirement in 1959.

Col. Shipley Thomas, a graduate of Yale University in 1915 and a reserve officer, first went to Washington to write a prisoner-of-war interrogation manual for Army Intelligence, later to a command post at Camp Ritchie, Md., an important officer-training center. A number of others whose capabilities were sorely missed in these hectic years were on leave for active duty in the Army, Navy, Air Force and other military branches, some of them in distant parts of the world.

Ford, Bacon & Davis was one of the five major construction and engineering organizations retained by the Government for the war's most sensational project—the undertaking which finally, on August 14, 1945, put an end to the war in the Pacific.

This was the Clinton Engineer Works at Oak Ridge, Tenn., pilot plant of the famed "Manhattan District" which handled the construction of the first atomic bomb. Ford, Bacon & Davis, in addition to its part in the initial construction, was retained to manage one section of the facilities for about 18 months, and during this period Everett S. Coldwell of FB&D was responsible for the work of about 3,000 employees.

The concept of obtaining energy from destruction of the atom was not, of course, scientifically new. By 1940, after years of work by scientists in several countries, the basic facts on the release and control of atomic energy were known. The Manhattan District was organized under Gen. Leslie R. Groves of the Army Corps of Engineers in June, 1942.

As far back as 1936, Ford, Bacon & Davis in a paper on electric power plant design, forecast the atomic technology that is now being put into actual use:

"The change may come through destruction of the atom. We are not so far away from such things."

The quote was later the subject of a check-up by wartime security officers, who wanted to know how Ford, Bacon & Davis had acquired this knowledge, which was in fact only an informed engineering deduction from publicly-available scientific and technical information.

The secrecy surrounding the "Manhattan District" and the whole atomic bomb development was tight and extremely well maintained. While many at Oak Ridge and a few top people in New York knew that something big was under way, their knowledge was limited to details of their own part in the work, and these details were top secret. They could and did guess, but they kept their guesses to themselves.

Even the test fission of the first bomb, at Alamogordo, N.M., in July, 1945, was kept under wraps. Only after the devastating Hiroshima blast on August 6 did the story become public. Then on August 9 came Nagasaki, and five days later the Japanese surrender, which was made official aboard the U.S.S. Missouri on September 2.

The war was over.

The post-war industrial transition to peacetime operations, which began in 1946, was in many ways as remarkable an achievement from a management standpoint, as the stupendous record which had been established in the war years.

Without any prolonged or painful readjustment, business quickly shifted to its hungry consumer markets and by dint of more hard work, had soon refilled its peacetime distribution pipelines with cars, cigarettes, steaks and butter, among countless other products. Not only domestic but European markets were supplied as the United States helped Europe to rebuild its shattered industrial structure.

New Jersey Zinc Company, a client for whom a wide range of assignments had been completed, was among those who needed work at this time on a number of projects, including preliminary design of a titanium pigment plant.

Commercial Solvents Corporation, another important client, commissioned major work at its Sterlington, La., chemical plant, including design and construction of alterations to modernize and expand capacity, and increase its operating efficiency. It was the first of a series of engineering projects for Commercial Solvents, and the start of a close working relationship with this leading chemical producer.

In the same year, Ford, Bacon & Davis was retained by Johns-Manville Corporation to design and construct, or supervise construction of, a number of major new facilities. The most important was a $9,000,000 insulating board plant at Natchez, Miss.

Other important jobs during this period included a study for Pennsylvania Salt Manufacturing Co., of its facilities at Wyandotte and as a result, modernization and construction of additional steam and power generating capacity at the plant.

For many companies whose operations had been vastly expanded by their wartime production assignments, transition was a sticky and complex problem. Could they profitably retain facilities and personnel? Were there large peacetime markets for their products and if so where? Could they shift economically into new products and new markets that would profitably utilize surplus capacity? Were acquisitions needed to strengthen some phase of the business, or provide an entry into a new market?

In some cases, companies were being retained by the Government to keep facilities on a stand-by basis. In others, the operating companies wished to acquire or lease the plants.

These factors generated a large volume of appraisals, market and other studies and detailed reports for Ford, Bacon & Davis, acting in some cases for the corporation concerned, in others for the Government.

After the emergency construction of industrial plants in the early 1940's, building was curtailed to make materials available for other purposes. By 1946, however, as materials again became available, the construction industry began to boom.

Industry was moving quickly to take full advantage of a "seller's market," particularly in consumer product lines, and needed new, low-cost facilities and increased capacity for the dynamic growth which loomed ahead.

During 1946, a flour specialty mill was designed for Pillsbury Mills, Inc., and its construction at Springfield, Ill., was under Ford, Bacon & Davis supervision. This was the first "premix" plant of its type, and was fully automated to operate with only a small supervisory staff. W. Ogden Johnson, graduate of the University of Michigan and later a vice president, was in charge of the job, which was one of a number of assignments for this client over the years. At this time, engineering studies were undertaken for the F. S. Royster Guano Company, involving preliminary layout of equipment, material flow and over-all design of a new 20,000-ton a year chemical fertilizer plant at Madison, Wisc. This was followed by design and construction, under the supervision of Robert S. Schultz, Jr., a graduate of Columbia University, and Harold P. Rounds, a graduate of Union College, of a new facility in line with the preliminary studies, which proved successful in terms of efficiency and low-cost operation.

Studies and reports were also made for National Biscuit Company, seeking to obtain improvements in design, equipment layout and materials handling in their bakeries in various sections of the country. This led, in 1947, to design and supervision

In its major post-war plant expansion and modernization program, National Biscuit Company retained FB&D for design and engineering work on a number of new facilities. One was the modern, highly-efficient bakery built in Portland, Ore., in 1949.

Pre-cast, insulated concrete wall panels developed by FB&D to eliminate costly masonry walls were first used on this 80,000 kw steam generating station designed and built for a Union Carbide subsidiary, at Marietta, Ohio, in 1948.

of construction of a new bakery at Portland, Ore., which incorporated a number of advanced techniques in efficient production and particularly in quality control, which is, of course, a vital factor in food processing.

One of the major examples of orderly transition to peacetime operations was that of Lockheed Aircraft Corporation, which was faced with the problem of cutting back a work force of about 90,000 employees to a 30,000 level. While many were wartime workers who could easily give up their jobs and did so, a proportionate shrinkage of the management group was replete with problems. Not the least of these was the selection and retention of the best-qualified men, so that the company would be strongly staffed for the competitive era that clearly lay ahead.

Ford, Bacon & Davis' work for Lockheed involved a broad over-all study, supplemented by detailed job description and job requirements for use by management in evaluation of personnel. In view of the impressive progress of the company since that time, the program must have been soundly conceived, and ably carried out by Lockheed management.

It was in 1946, too, that Ford, Bacon & Davis embarked on a series of major projects for Electro Metallurgical Company, a division of Union Carbide, involving design and supervision of construction of large power plant projects, and design of five metallurgical alloy plants.

The first was an 80,000 kw steam power generating plant at Ashtabula, Ohio. The following year a 40,000 kw extension was built at the steam station in Alloy, West Va. In 1948, another 80,000 kw steam electric generating station was built at Marietta, Ohio. Later, capacity was doubled at the Marietta and Ashtabula plants.

It was in connection with the design of the Marietta facilities that Ford, Bacon & Davis initiated some research to find a satisfactory but less costly substitute for conventional masonry walls. As a result pre-cast panels were developed which were made of a core of efficient insulating material, sandwiched between thin layers of concrete.

These were fabricated by production line methods, and the cost of the new material, put in place, was a third lower than the 12-inch masonry walls which would otherwise have been required. The panels proved to be not only a satisfactory material for the purpose, but gave the structure a neat and attractive appearance.

Another job in this series of undertakings for Union Carbide involved large additions to its chemical plant facilities at Institute, West Va., operated by a subsidiary, Carbide & Carbon Chemicals Company, now Union Carbide Chemicals Company.

In the early 1940's, Ford, Bacon & Davis had done important work for the city of Galveston, Tex., in a program to upgrade and expand its water supply and sewage systems. This became valuable background in 1947 when two companies with large operations in Texas City—Union Carbide and Pan American Refining Corp., a subsidiary of Standard Oil of Indiana—retained Ford, Bacon & Davis to design and supervise construction of a system for the Galveston County Water Company. On completion of the project, which involved a survey over a wide surrounding area of the state to locate adequate sources, Ford, Bacon & Davis was retained to manage and staff a new water company for the first nine months of operation.

During the war years, of course, reports, appraisals and feasibility studies were largely shelved while the nation concentrated on all-out production based entirely on military needs and with cost a secondary consideration. The staff which normally engaged in report work, "drafted" for essential construction and production for the duration, had to be rebuilt in the late 1940's to handle the revival in survey and report assignments.

In 1946, a group of prominent citizens of Metropolitan Philadelphia formed a committee to sponsor a complete survey of all available hospital facilities in the area. Probably for reasons having to do with major past achievements in the city where it was founded, Ford, Bacon & Davis was selected to handle the project. An outstanding hospital and medical consultant was engaged, and over a period of about a year, a survey and report were completed under the direction of Harold V. Coes, a vice-president, with recommendations for meeting current and future requirements of the community.

Among the sizeable valuation assignments which developed at this time were the appraisal of physical properties of International Petroleum, Ltd., in Peru, and commercial valuations made for Imperial Oil and Shell Oil in Canada.

Much work to the south of the United States was developing at this time, and to handle some of it, a Mexican subsidiary, Ford, Bacon & Davis, S.A., was formed. The work originated largely at the Bank of Mexico and its allied agency, Nacional Financiera, S.A. A number of comprehensive engineering studies were made for these interests, including plant feasibility studies, and programs to expand and upgrade various types of industries.

One was a survey of the sugar industry in Mexico, which covered not only the agronomy, soils and entomology of the cane-growing areas, but a detailed inventory and appraisal of the physical condition of all the sugar mills in the country.

A study of the nation's fisheries industry led to important conservation measures, which in turn resulted in a more orderly development of this rich national resource. In the field of transportation, a feasibility study was made of a proposed railroad over and through the Sierra Madre Mountains, to connect Durango with the port of Mazatlan, which included a survey of the route and location studies for terminal and other facilities needed for efficient operation.

Perhaps as important, basically, as any other single project was a study of the Mexican postal system, which led to substantial improvements in the service provided by this vital communications medium.

This work was under the general supervision of Coleman R. Sample, and Henry C. Drewes, a graduate of Cooper Union.

These various assignments required from time to time a large number of engineers and other specialists. During these years the organization accumulated a huge file of data, and became a recognized expert on the Mexican economy and the opportunities that the country offers for industrial development.

Following the war, U.S. Government work had declined sharply, as was to be expected, but Government had become a more important factor than ever before in business generally. The Army Corps of Engineers in 1949 commissioned Ford, Bacon & Davis to make an extensive study to determine and point up general areas which, in view of all relevant factors, would be the most suitable for large-scale production of synthetic liquid fuels, in the event of future need. Since a thorough report was desired, the assignment involved surveys covering some 37 states and Alaska, where appropriate raw materials were economically located.

It was on April 16, 1947, that a ship loaded with supposedly harmless ammonium nitrate lay smoldering in the harbor at Texas City with firemen working to extinguish a cargo fire. Suddenly, it blew up and virtually annihilated the waterfront, killing several hundred people.

A nearby plant of Monsanto Chemical Company was badly damaged. Ford, Bacon & Davis was called in by the Oil Assurance Association to determine for the underwriters the insurable value of the properties damaged or destroyed.

For some years, Ford, Bacon & Davis had been leaders in urging upon the gas industry the economic advantages of large-diameter, long-distance pipe lines from major gas producing areas to large concentrations of population and industry. The firm had, by this time, of course, a long background of successful experience in pipeline work, and was a major factor in the design and construction of both oil and gas pipelines, as well as pumping and other operating facilities.

It was logical that, when the firm of Dillon Read & Co., was planning permanent financing for Texas Eastern Transmission Company, which had acquired the "Big Inch" and "Little Inch" systems built by the Government during the war, Ford, Bacon & Davis should be called in to assist in preparation of the prospectus and registration papers in connection with the public offering of Texas Eastern securities.

The two systems were built for moving both crude and refined petroleum products from the Gulf Coast to the big industrial areas in the Middle Atlantic states. Ford, Bacon & Davis had constructed important eastern extensions of the lines.

Texas Eastern had converted the two systems for transporting gas, to be sold to the large gas utility companies serving the northeast, and in some cases directly to large industrial users.

This spectacular development focused national attention on the changed economic situation affecting the use of natural gas as a fuel, not only for large-scale industrial purposes but for heating all types of buildings and for household heating and cooking.

The price of coal, in which labor is an important factor, had been pushed steadily up to a point where natural gas could effectively compete with it in many major markets. Furthermore, the improved technology of moving gas in large-diameter pipe lines had cut costs so that it was feasible to transmit natural gas from the mid-Continent and Gulf Coast fields to large eastern markets previously served with manufactured gas, or with natural gas from the Appalachian fields.

For many local or small regional gas distributing companies, the development was a new lease on life and meant the difference between profit and loss in their operations. The higher heating values of natural gas (about 1,000 Btu's per cubic foot compared with around 580 Btu's for manufactured gas) had the effect of practically doubling the capacity of their distribution systems in terms of heat units available to customers.

Thus in the late 1940's, a boom in natural gas pipe line

construction got under way which in some ways was comparable in importance to the great railroad expansion following the Civil War.

The mileage of gas transmission lines in the United States increased from 77,300 miles in 1945 to 157,600 miles in 1957, or more than double in a 12 year period. Actually, this expansion was much greater than mileage figures indicate, since the trend was toward much larger diameters so that capacity increased even faster.

Beginning in 1947, Ford, Bacon & Davis was appointed to serve as engineers for Michigan Wisconsin Pipe Line Company, and Austin Field Pipe Line Company, on a major pipe line project—the 1,584-mile line, primarily of 24 and 22-inch pipe, from the Hugoton gas field at the Texas-Oklahoma border, to Detroit, Milwaukee and Green Bay.

Ford, Bacon & Davis made the initial studies to establish feasibility of the project, then assisted in obtaining a certificate of convenience and necessity from the Federal Power Commission. With these preliminaries accomplished, the firm designed and supervised construction of the pipeline itself, meanwhile building with its own crews, the compressor stations, dehydration plants, meter and regulator stations and other essential facilities for the entire project.

The main line was designed for a working pressure of 970 pounds per square inch, and the compressor stations furnished an aggregate of 139,200 horsepower to move the gas at a rated capacity of 343,000,000 cubic feet per day. Following completion of the work, Ford, Bacon & Davis was consultant to the owners in setting up a permanent operating organization for the system, which represented an investment of some $120,000,000.

The huge job was under the general supervision of Edgar G. Hill, and both Mr. Hill and the Firm took considerable pride in the fact that the owner, sometimes referred to as "Mish-Wish," insisted on naming the largest compressor plant on the line the Edgar G. Hill Station.

One aspect of the project which added substantially to its economic efficiency was the use of large depleted natural gas fields north of Grand Rapids, Mich., for storage purposes, which allows the transmission system to operate at approximately 100% load factor on a year-round basis, accumulating reserves in the off-peak months for heavy cold weather demand.

George I. Rhodes was a prime mover in getting the companies concerned interested in this aspect of the project, and working out the various problems involved.

The project was placed in successful operation in November, 1949, and Ford, Bacon & Davis since then has served as consultant to the owner and its subsidiary companies, including Michigan Consolidated Gas Company, for which various other natural gas facilities have been constructed from time to time.

In the same year, Ford, Bacon & Davis was retained on a project which was to involve costly litigation before it could be completed. Algonquin Gas Transmission Co., of Boston, was organized to bring natural gas into New England, where both climate and heavy concentration of industries provide a large and relatively stable basic market.

Following surveys and reports on feasibility of a line which would supply local gas distributors in New England cities, Ford, Bacon & Davis assisted in preparation and presentation of the Algonquin case before the Federal Power Commission, to obtain the required certificate of convenience and necessity.

The application was actively contested by Tennessee Gas Transmission Company and its subsidiary, Northeastern Gas Transmission. The FPC decided the issue by splitting the area to be served between Algonquin and Northeastern.

The design and supervision of construction of the Algonquin line was assigned to Ford, Bacon & Davis. Extending from Lambertville, N.J., to Boston, the 523 miles of 24 and 26-inch transmission system cost approximately $51,500,000. The investment, once made, of course, involved charges for interest and overhead of something on the order of $500,000 a month.

Just before the job was completed, work was stopped by court order, on the plea of Tennessee Gas and Northeastern that they had not been given due process to intervene in the FPC proceedings which granted the Algonquin certificate. The case went to the U.S. Supreme Court, which upheld the Tennessee Gas plea and required the Federal Power Commission to re-open the case. After re-hearing the Algonquin application and the opposition case, the FPC reaffirmed its original findings and Algonquin was free to complete the project.

Meantime, for 11 months the costly project had stood idle, while interest charges continued. The setting aside of the FPC certificate by the courts created a precedent which brought consternation in the pipe line industry, since it opened a new and not insignificant element of risk in such undertakings.

In connection with the development of this major transmission system, Ford, Bacon & Davis was later retained by a number of local New England gas utilities to assist on various problems including recommendations on equipment and facilities needed to handle distribution of the natural gas; preliminary construction cost estimates, and design and supervision of construction of tap lines and other facilities required to connect their local systems to Algonquin's line. These utilities included Hartford Gas Company, Providence Gas Company, Worcester Gas Light Company, Newport Gas Light Co., North Attleboro Gas Company and the Norwich Gas and Electric Department.

Natural gas projects were an increasingly important phase of Ford, Bacon & Davis work during these years as the economic advantages of this highly-efficient energy source began to gain wide acceptance among prospective customers.

While the big Algonquin project was under way, smaller engineering teams were busy elsewhere. In Virginia, Commonwealth Natural Gas retained Ford, Bacon & Davis for the job of bringing natural gas to Richmond and Norfolk from a transmission line about 150 miles away. In addition to certification, the work involved design and supervision of construction of about 150 miles of pipe line and operating facilities. A similar assignment came from Roanoke Pipe Line Co., involving about 30 miles of connecting line.

A number of feasibility reports were made for various local and regional gas distributing companies, which by setting up cost estimates against revenue potentials, established a realistic basis for the proposed investment, in terms of future earning power. This work extended into Canada, and clients included Consumers' Gas Company of Toronto, Hamilton By-Products Coke Ovens Ltd. of Hamilton, Ontario, and later Quebec Hydro-Electric Commission of Montreal.

A basic operating problem of the gas transmission industry is the normal, seasonal fluctuation in customer demand, which involves a wide disparity in the rate of consumption over a 12-month period. Since much of the business is based on non-interruptible service in which the customer is, in effect, guaranteed a supply equal to maximum requirements on a year-round basis, substantial investment is required for pipeline capacity to meet peak loads, even though part of this capacity will be unused for much of the year.

The obvious solution is large storage facilities close to the market which, filled during periods of slack demand, can be drawn on in peak periods. This makes possible economical construction of a transmission line that, operating at approximately full capacity on a year-round basis, brings in, either for consumption or storage, the volume needed to supply the annual market. The end result is higher earnings for the utility and lower rates for the customer. Maximum utilization of installed capacity, as in any business, means lower costs.

Ford, Bacon & Davis was a pioneer in the use of depleted natural gas reservoirs for storage purposes in order to gain these

cost advantages for clients. Since such reservoirs were useless for
any other purpose, they provided ideal facilities with very little
added investment.

The firm on its own account had done extensive research into
the practical engineering problems involved in this concept, and

*Largest in the world when it was conceived, designed and
built by FB&D in the early 1950's, the huge Oakford, Pa.,
natural gas reservoirs under these pumping and control facilities hold over 100 billion cubic feet to meet peak winter
demand.*

as a result suggested to Consolidated Natural Gas Company the
possibility of using huge depleted reservoirs near Oakford, Pa., a
short distance northeast of Pittsburgh.

As a result, in 1949 Ford, Bacon & Davis was asked to assist in
obtaining an FPC certificate of convenience and necessity, and
in 1950 was retained by New York State Natural Gas Corporation, a subsidiary of Consolidated, and by Texas Eastern Transmission Corporation, to design and construct the facilities.

At the time, Oakford was the largest underground natural gas storage project in the world, consisting of two huge pockets, the upper one with a working capacity of 85 billion cubic feet of gas, a lower one holding some 20 billion cubic feet under much higher pressure, for a total of 105 billion cubic feet.

The project, completed on schedule at a cost of about $10,600,000, included a 30,000-hp compressor station, dehydration plant and auxiliary facilities near Delmont, Pa., some 25 miles east of Pittsburgh.

This was one of the last major construction jobs of the 1940's, and did nothing to diminish the Ford, Bacon & Davis reputation for sound engineering which emphasizes the basic objective of every business—maximum results from minimum investment required to obtain them.

Report work of various types was handled in volume in the post-war years. One of the more challenging jobs was an assignment in 1950 to make an engineering survey and report on the feasibility and other engineering aspects of a proposed development by Sherritt-Gordon Mines, Ltd. This was the Lynn Lake project, principally for mining nickel and copper from properties located in northern Manitoba.

Included in the proposed development was a refinery to be built at Fort Saskatchewan, Alberta, close to supplies of natural gas which would provide economical fuel for the operation.

At the time Ford, Bacon & Davis was called in to evaluate and report on the program, exploration work was well under way at Lynn Lake. A shaft had been sunk and a small work force was established at the mine site. A railroad was planned, but not yet built, and the only means of reaching the wilderness area was by plane or, in the winter months, by tractor train.

Heavy supplies were brought in by these "snow trains" including houses from the site of prior operations about 150 miles south in Sherridon, Manitoba. When the Ford, Bacon & Davis men first flew in, they could see a tractor train crawling along in the wintry terrain below. At the new town of Lynn Lake, when they arrived, the two most important installations had already been completed—a school and a curling rink, an essential part of community life in any Canadian town during the long winters.

It was in 1949, toward the close of the war decade, that Ford, Bacon & Davis undertook another major assignment in Canada —studies leading to the design and supervision of construction of a new lead smelter at Trail, B.C., for Consolidated Mining & Smelting Co. of Canada, Ltd., a large producer of lead, zinc, silver and other metals. Consolidated is controlled by the Canadian Pacific Railway, and is part of the far-flung interests in "natural resources" operations which are an increasingly important part of Canadian Pacific's global transportation empire.

The Firm started working initially for Asbestos Corporation Ltd., at this time, on problems concerning its mines and mills at Thetford Mines, Quebec. Over a period of years, Ford, Bacon & Davis made a number of engineering studies and handled design and construction for this client, and for other operators in the area, which is the source of most of the asbestos mined in North America. At one point, this work included the preparation of plans for the complete relocation of a railroad and main highway, and part of the town, in order to allow the mines to expand their operations.

To handle continued growth during the decade of the 1940's, and to replace the men who had reached retirement age, several important additions were made to the engineering staff. William B. Poor, who came to the firm in 1948, brought with him a broad background in gas pipe line construction and operation. A graduate of Ohio State University he became a vice-president in 1953, and a director two years later.

During the 1940's a number of other key men came into the organization. Durwood X. Ellet, graduate of the University of Illinois, joined the Construction Corporation in 1941, the same year W. Ogden Johnson, a specialist in design and industrial engineering, came with the Firm. George P. Breece joined the

FB&D accounting staff in 1947, to be elected secretary-treasurer of both Ford, Bacon & Davis and the Construction Corporation in 1956, and a director in 1962.

Mr. Towers, who became president in 1942, and chairman early in 1946, had devoted time, while president, to developing a new concept of stock ownership in the company for key employees. In past years, as time went by, more and more stock came to be held by those no longer active in the business, or by their heirs.

Recognizing the importance of stock control, in a personal service enterprise, by those responsible for day-to-day operation of the business, Mr. Towers, working with Henry F. Storck, secretary-treasurer from 1931 until his death in 1956, devised a plan which, adopted at a special stockholders meeting in November, 1943, became known as the Tenure Plan.

The capitalization was revised to create a new class of voting common stock, called Tenure Stock, which was made available to those in key positions, to be held only during their active employment by the company. On retirement, this voting stock was convertible into non-voting preferred shares. Thus the majority of voting common stock was in the hands of those who were directly responsible for current operations and future growth.

It was on January 1, 1949, that Everett S. Coldwell, who had been executive vice-president since 1947, was elected president. Mr. Coldwell, who had been an important factor in FB&D's progress during these years, continued as president until the end of 1956, and as chairman until his retirement in 1959.

The rapid growth of business during the late 1940's led to some disquiet among businessmen, who feared the economy might be heading into serious and "inevitable" post-war reaction. The reaction came in 1949, but it was short-lived.

Early in 1950, President Truman ordered development of the hydrogen bomb, a far more powerful atomic weapon than those

EVERETT S. COLDWELL
Director, 1942–1959
President, 1949–1957
Chairman, 1949–1959

dropped on Japan. At mid-year, the Korean situation flared into active combat as North Korean forces pushed south, U.S. ground forces were landed at Inchon and by year-end, a state of national emergency had been declared.

This brought a sharp upsurge in business and the various indices of economic activity resumed their long, persistent up-trend —destined to establish staggering new records as the nation's awesome industrial growth quickly regained its momentum.

VII

Industry Moves into World Markets
as Post-War Expansion Drives Ahead ˎ

W AR THREATS hung grimly over the nation on January 1, 1951, as Chinese Communist troops broke through defenses around Seoul, took Inchon and Kimpo airfield and forced abandonment of Seoul three days later. U.S. armed forces, doubled since the outbreak of the Korean hostilities in 1950, had been increased to 2,900,000 men. Seoul was recaptured from the Reds on March 14.

The Federal budget estimate, including defense spending of $41.4 billion, forecast a deficit of over $6 billion for the year. Margin requirements on the New York Stock Exchange were boosted from 50 to 75 per cent by the Federal Reserve Board of Governors, but security prices continued to rise. It was in 1949 that the nation's security markets, after nearly three years of trading in a narrow price range, had taken off on what was to become the longest and by far the most spectacular boom in U.S. history. By the end of the decade, security prices were at the highest level since 1929, and headed higher.

[141]

Reflecting in part the long succession of Federal budget deficits financed through the banking system, prices paid by consumers had risen some 60 per cent since 1940. The Federal debt, which under the impact of war had soared from $53.6 billion at the beginning of 1941 to $266.4 billion in 1950, was headed for $322 billion by the end of the decade as Government steadily expanded its operations.

Partial mobilization had little or no adverse effect on technological progress in non-defense areas. Television in 1951 scored two important "firsts"—a commercial color broadcast by CBS, and a transcontinental broadcast of President Truman's talk at the opening in September of the Japanese Peace Treaty Conference in San Francisco—which helped turn a one-time enemy into a valuable and powerful ally.

In October, transcontinental dial telephone service began experimentally at Englewood, N.J., and some two months later, in December, the U.S. Reactor Testing Station in Idaho produced the first electric power from atomic energy.

A population of 151,700,000 in 1950, increasing at the rate of 2,800,000 a year, would reach 180,000,000 by 1960.

The chemical industry among others was expanding rapidly and the Ford, Bacon & Davis engineering and construction departments were busy as clients stepped up their operations and expanded their facilities to meet the demands of a rising population and a steadily higher standard of living in every income group.

Major projects for Union Carbide were still under way. In 1951 through 1953, two additional 40,000 kw generating units were installed at the Electro Metallurgical steam power station at Ashtabula, which Ford, Bacon & Davis designed, and supervised while under construction during 1947–1949. Various other work was also carried out at this location, including the design of new carbide and silicon furnaces.

In a five-year period to 1954, a big, $45 million alloy complex was designed for Union Carbide, at Marietta, Ohio, which was based on Carbide's own processes. The facilities included 60,000-ton low-carbon ferrochrome and 2,000-ton electrolytic chromium plants. W. Ogden Johnson was in charge of FB&D work on this major project, which continued in close cooperation with the client's own engineers during the construction.

During this period, too, Carbide & Carbon Chemicals Division needed added capacity at the large chemical plant in Texas City on which Ford, Bacon & Davis had worked back in 1940, and the Firm was assigned to construct the required extensions.

It was in the early 1950's that Commercial Solvents decided to enlarge its Sterlington, La., plant and Ford, Bacon & Davis was retained in 1951 for design and construction of facilities to increase production of ammonia and methanol. This work also included design and construction of a new unit for production of ammonium nitrate, as well as construction work on a nitrogen solution plant and a nitrate pilot plant.

A number of new plants for manufacture of nitrates were being built in various sections of the country at this time, to supply fertilizer for the intensified farming methods that resulted from acreage reduction under Federal crop limitation programs.

The chemical industry was expanding in other areas as well. In 1951, Ford, Bacon & Davis designed and built for an old client, United Carbon Company, a furnace-type oil-base carbon black plant at Franklin, La. In the following year a new highly automated processing and manufacturing plant was designed and built for Dearborn Chemical Company at Lake Zurich, Ill., to produce water-treating and detergent chemicals.

It was in 1953 that Ford, Bacon & Davis got into "show business," being retained by Metro-Goldwyn-Mayer for a cost-control survey of that company's big studios at Culver City, Calif., which with a facade of classic Greek architecture, replete with columns, are very impressive in appearance.

This assignment produced a sequel to the story about the camouflage which MGM had installed at the big Douglas aircraft plants in Santa Monica early in the War, so that FB&D engineers thought their plane was landing in the city streets.

After completing their artistic effort on the Douglas plants, it seems MGM officials had decided that some similar move should be made to protect their own property in case of an enemy air raid. Permission was sought from the Army Air Force officers in charge of this activity, to apply camouflage on the huge Culver City lot.

The answer was immediately forthcoming, and definitive:

"No. You are the decoy."

Needless to say, this somewhat disquieting tactical concept was not publicized, and MGM employees continued about their business happily unaware of their sacrificial role in the war.

National Biscuit Company again retained Ford, Bacon & Davis in 1953, for the design of a new bakery at Philadelphia which was part of a comprehensive, nation-wide program of expansion and modernization of its plant facilities, to obtain more efficient production, and upgrade quality in line with post-war market trends.

About this time, two major companies—Pittsburgh Consolidation Coal Company and Cleveland Electric Illuminating Company—had become actively interested in the economics and the practical engineering aspects of moving coal by pipe line.

In 1954, Ford, Bacon & Davis was retained by Pittsburgh Consolidation to make the investigation and do preliminary engineering on a proposed 108-mile, 10-inch coal slurry system from Cadiz, Ohio, where the mine was located, to the Eastlake station of Cleveland Electric Illuminating on Lake Erie.

In addition to preliminary engineering, which included surveying and mapping the proposed route, a cost-of-service study of the project was made, along with an opinion on the capacity and adequacy of the system and its estimated initial cost.

These studies indicated a worthwhile payout for the project and, in 1955, Ford, Bacon & Davis was assigned responsibility for engineering design and supervision of construction of the system, which required three pumping stations to move the finely ground coal, suspended in water, at an economical delivery rate. Facilities for draining off water and drying the coal were constructed by Cleveland Electric.

The pumping of solids suspended in liquid was not new from an engineering standpoint, and there was a body of technical knowledge on the subject dealing with such problems as abrasion of pipe and pumping equipment, all of which was thoroughly investigated in the planning.

The size and potential economic importance of the actual project, however, attracted intense interest in engineering and transportation circles, and no little attention in the general press as well. The method had not, until then, had any major application and this was, for all practical purposes, a pioneer move.

To Ford, Bacon & Davis engineers familiar with the problems involved, it appears that economics will increasingly favor the overland pumping of solids whenever a slurry of fine sizes is desirable (as in this case) and especially where low-cost water or rail transportation is not already available.

The Cadiz-Cleveland system proved out in operation. The pipeline had the added, and not unexpected, effect of stimulating energetic and effective action on the part of major rail carriers dependent on coal, to upgrade their services and reduce tariffs to utilities with such devices as shuttle unit trains. These unit-trains carry coal directly from mine to power station using loading and unloading facilities which provide almost immediate turnaround of trains so that efficiency approaches that of an endless belt.

Since coal is, however, the most plentiful form of cheap fossil energy available, the long-term potentials of this pioneering pipeline development cannot be over-emphasized, even though rail and water transportation may well remain competitive in many areas. Implicit in the successful use of pipelines for coal is the prospect of low-cost transportation to areas without adequate water or rail service, not only of coal but other solids used in large volume.

The nation's huge network of gas and oil pipelines may well have ultimate value far beyond the eventual exhaustion of the reserves for which they were built.

Development of liquid and gas fuels from coal, which is feasible once the demand arises, would similarly prolong the usefulness of the pipeline system, with suitable modifications.

The problem of urban traffic congestion was already becoming acute in the larger cities of the United States during the mid-1950's. In 1954, the Port of New York Authority, which the Firm earlier had helped to create, commissioned a study and report on the estimated growth of bus traffic entering and leaving New York City. The assignment also covered a feasibility report on the economics of constructing additional facilities for the Port Authority Bus Terminal.

The following year, the Metropolitan Rapid Transit Commission and the Port Authority retained the Firm to make a study and related report on common carrier interstate bus transportation between the city and the communities west of the Hudson River which are considered part of the New York metropolitan region. Designed to serve as a basis for long-range future planning, the study took into account projected growth and economic development through 1975.

During 1954, construction fell off slightly from the $28 billion a year peak reached in 1953, but in 1955 the economy rebounded sharply and for the next three years, industry invested in new plant and equipment at an unprecedented rate. In addition to increased capacity, manufacturers of nearly every type needed facilities for the new products that were emerging from intensive post-war research and development.

[146]

The demand for modern plant, machinery and equipment was intensified by the pressure of rising labor costs, which could only be offset by increased productivity that reduced the labor content of the end product. Engineers, particularly those with experience in areas relating to aviation or electronics, were in short supply as Government demands increased for research, development and production of defense and other material and equipment.

Among many important specialized companies affected by the continual upsurge of business in the 1950's, Veeder-Root, Incorporated, of Hartford, was outgrowing its plant there and in 1954 retained Ford, Bacon & Davis to investigate the feasibility of moving certain operations to a new location. The Company, which manufactures a wide variety of counting devices and other industrial controls, also desired a survey of possible new sites for the proposed expansion.

Ford, Bacon & Davis prepared a plant layout closely geared to efficient work flow, together with estimates of capital costs and projected savings in operating expenses. As a result of its report in the following year, the Firm was assigned to complete the detailed planning and design and supervise construction of a manufacturing facility at Altoona, Pa., where the Ford, Bacon & Davis plant location survey indicated that optimum advantages in labor supply and other key factors existed.

During 1956–1957, a similar project was undertaken for Homelite Division of Textron, Inc., which covered an initial study of possible new plant sites, an estimate of the capital investment involved and projected operating economies to be obtained from the new facility.

In 1955, a project was undertaken for Roddis Plywood Corp. at Arcata, Calif., involving the design and supervision of construction of a plant specially designed to use a new European (Behr) process in the production of hardboard from wood chips and synthetic resins. Utilizing extremely high pressures and temperatures, the process makes a superior product, suitable for table and counter tops and similar applications where durability and damage-resistance are important.

Some years later the plant, which provided low-cost production in scheduled quantities, was sold to Weyerhauser Lumber Company. It was a logical extension of that Company's long range program to obtain maximum economic value from its vast timber reserves, which like most such U.S. forest resources today, are operated as permanent "tree farms," on which timber is harvested as a crop, only at the annual growth rate.

In 1955, too, Ford, Bacon & Davis was retained by Owens-Corning Fiberglass Corporation to make engineering studies and reports. Initially, a new building was required to house the company's facilities at Newark, Ohio, which included four of the largest furnaces in the world producing molten glass for fiber production. It is prohibitively expensive to shut down this type of operation for any reason. Consequently, a plan was evolved and carried out which involved construction of a new and larger building, some 200 by 276 feet, with a maximum clear height of 59 feet, over and around the original structure. Production continued uninterrupted while the construction was under way, and, after piping, wiring and other services had been rearranged and connected, the old structure was dismantled and removed, again without interfering with the normal operation of the furnaces.

Another valuable client, the Columbia Southern Chemical Corp., a subsidiary of Pittsburgh Plate Glass Company, retained the firm in 1955 to make a study and report in connection with waste disposal problems at its Barberton, Ohio, plant, which was one of a series of assignments from Columbia Southern over a period of years.

The following year, 1956, Pittsburgh Consolidation Coal Company retained the firm to make engineering studies, together with preliminary planning on a large low-temperature coal carbonization and tar processing installation at Cresap, West Va. The project included site preparation for six processing units and design and supervision of construction of a coke calcining plant.

During 1956, too, the Firm again became active in the aluminum industry, which is completely dependent on low-cost electric power. The initial assignment was a report to Olin Mathieson Chemical Corporation on the feasibility of an aluminum reduction plant to be constructed by Ormet Corporation, jointly owned by Olin Mathieson and Revere Copper & Brass, Inc.

The project was based on availability of low-cost water transportation to move bauxite from South America to an alumina plant which was built on the Mississippi River at Burnside, La., and to move the alumina to the reduction plant constructed on the Ohio River at Omal, Ohio, close to a major supply of coal.

This was one of the first big aluminum projects to use a coal-fired steam generating plant for power, as distinct from a hydro-electric power source, obtainable nowadays only in remote, undeveloped areas of the world. Proximity to large markets for aluminum ingot, and a high degree of efficiency in the steam-generating plant, combined to offset the power-cost differential.

About this time, the Firm was serving as consulting engineers to the Dominican Republic in connection with a bauxite concession in that country held by Alcoa.

Then Harvey Machine Company of Los Angeles, now Harvey Aluminum, retained the Firm for a series of assignments. The first covered a report and design checks on plans for an aluminum plant to be built near the Hungry Horse hydro-electric development in Montana. As construction was getting under way, the property and rights were sold to Anaconda.

Harvey shortly afterward signed an agreement to obtain power from the huge Bonneville development for another aluminum project at The Dalles, Ore., and again called in Ford, Bacon & Davis to assist on reports and preliminary planning and

Rising out of the Canadian prairies at Medicine Hat, Alberta, a big ammonium complex fertilizer plant was built by FB&D in 1955–1956 for Northwest Nitro-Chemicals, Ltd., following feasibility studies of this and other proposed facilities.

design. (This area in Oregon gets its unusual name from the French-derived word "dalles," meaning the walls of a dell or gorge.)

Continuing to expand, Commercial Solvents Corporation in the mid-1950's decided to go ahead with a nitroparaffin plant at its Sterlington, La., property. Working with the client's engineering staff, Ford, Bacon & Davis participated in design work on this project, and then built the new facilities.

Another major project of the time was a proposed ammonium nitrate and ammonium phosphate fertilizer plant for Northwest Nitro Chemicals Limited, a majority-owned affiliate of Commercial Solvents, to be located at Medicine Hat, Alberta. Following a feasibility study, Ford, Bacon & Davis in 1955 designed the ammonium nitrate unit, and managed the construction of the entire complex. This huge facility, which occupies some 30% of its 2,300-acre site, was completed at a cost of about $22,000,-000 and went into operation late in 1956. Commercial Solvents has since acquired practically complete ownership.

During the years these varied industrial projects were under way, the Firm was equally busy with major pipeline construction, and also found itself with a growing volume of overseas assignments covering a wide range of engineering work.

Demand for natural gas grew rapidly in the 1950's, and the industry's revenues rose from $2.5 billion in 1950 to $8.7 billion in 1960. To serve its expanding markets, Southern Natural Gas was pushing ahead on major expansion programs. In 1950–1951, Ford, Bacon & Davis was assigned the engineering and supervision of construction of some 800 miles of pipe line, along with design and construction of new compressor stations and additions to existing stations.

The following year, in Southern's 1952–1953 expansion program, Ford, Bacon & Davis provided engineering services and supervision of construction for 1,034 miles of 24-inch line, as well as design and construction of five new compressor stations, a dehydration plant, and a distillate reduction plant.

Meantime, the Firm was retained by Oklahoma Mississippi River Products Line, Inc., for a feasibility study covering engineering, commercial and financial aspects of a proposed oil products line and other facilities from its Oklahoma refineries to the Mississippi River. On the basis of a favorable report, Ford, Bacon & Davis was retained to design and supervise construction, in 1953–1954, of a 400-mile 10 inch pipeline from Duncan, Okla., to West Memphis, Ark., which involved an investment of about $18,000,000, including a Tulsa connection. Fred C. Culpepper, Jr., now a vice-president of the Construction Corporation, was project manager.

About this time, the Mid-Valley Pipe Line was under consideration as a 1,000-mile crude oil carrier from Texas to Ohio, to be a joint enterprise of Standard Oil of Ohio and Sun Oil. The Firm was retained to report on the economics and feasibility of the project.

The biggest pipeline job of this period was the large-diameter natural gas line from southern Louisiana to the Detriot market, 1,164-mile project which included 971 miles of 30-inch main line pipe and a 122-mile lateral connecting with the Michigan Wisconsin system in western Michigan. For this work, the American Louisiana Pipe Line Company, a subsidiary of American Natural Gas Company, retained Ford, Bacon & Davis for preliminary engineering services and to assist in the application to the Federal Power Commission for a certificate of convenience and necessity.

The project was built in 1955, with the Firm responsible for engineering, design and supervision of construction. It was a $130,000,000 job and involved five major river crossings in addition to the usual problems incident to obtaining a right of way through favorable terrain, to hold down costs.

In the same year, other Ford, Bacon & Davis pipe line men were working on several jobs for Texas Gas Transmission Company, which included construction of a number of natural gas compressor stations to boost capacity on parts of its system.

In 1956, the Firm was working as a consultant to Michigan Wisconsin Pipe Line Company, in connection with proposed expansion of its system, and also designed and supervised construction of pipe line extensions and designed and built two new compressor stations.

At this time, Washington and Oregon were two of the few remaining states which still had no supply of natural gas and there was an increasing demand for this highly efficient fuel, reflecting rapid industrial growth in the Pacific Northwest. Back in 1949, Ford, Bacon & Davis had started working for Westcoast Transmission Co., Ltd., initially on a feasibility report covering a proposed pipe line from Alberta and British Columbia fields to markets in British Columbia and across the border to populated areas of western Washington and Oregon.

The Firm assisted in presenting the case before the Federal Power Commission and, after a long series of bitterly contested hearings, spread over an 18-month period, the certificate was awarded to the competing Pacific Northwest Pipe Line Corporation, which planned to bring the gas from the San Juan Basin or "Four Corners" area (the unique junction of state borders between Utah, Colorado, Arizona and New Mexico).

However, after the Certificate had been awarded to Pacific Northwest, it became clear that additional gas would be needed to supply the demand, and construction of the pipeline from the Alberta and British Columbia fields, south to the Canadian border, near Vancouver, was authorized. Ford, Bacon & Davis was retained as Westcoast Transmission engineers and representatives in the construction of the pipeline from the Peace River area some 650 miles south to the U.S. border. The line included a 233-mile gathering system at the field, later extended to other producing wells. Ford, Bacon & Davis also designed the compressor and measuring stations on the system.

On this same project, the Firm also served as engineering-construction manager for Pacific Petroleums Ltd., in the building of a gas processing plant near Taylor, British Columbia, the starting point of the Westcoast main transmission line.

This project immediately made possible added gas distribution in British Columbia, and Inland Natural Gas Company, Ltd., was formed for the purpose. Inland retained Ford, Bacon & Davis to make the necessary engineering and economic studies required for financing, and to design and supervise construction of a 304-mile 6-inch to 12-inch transmission system, as well as 60 miles of 4-inch distribution mains serving communities in British Columbia.

Over the years Ford, Bacon & Davis has acted in a consulting capacity to a large number of cities, states and other public entities on electric power projects and problems and has designed and built major power facilities for them.

For the South Carolina Public Service Authority, FB&D designed and managed construction of a new 80,000 kw steam-electric generating station at Moncks Corner, S.C., in 1955, one of many highly-efficient FB&D designs over the years.

Back in 1951–1953, the Firm designed and managed construction of an 80,000 kw steam generating station at Pinopolis on Lake Moultrie, for the South Carolina Public Service Authority, and assisted in start-up operations of the plant. Other assignments on public power facilities during the 1950's included services to the City of Monroe, La.; the City of Seattle; Washington State Power Commission; City of Tacoma, Wash.; the Salt River project in Phoenix, Ariz., and the Bonneville Power Administration, a Federal agency.

Other government business, particularly studies, appraisals, and reports, became important during the 1950's. In 1955 the Firm undertook an extensive study of the overhaul and repair facilities of the Navy's Bureau of Aeronautics.

Partly as a result of the government foreign aid program, Ford, Bacon & Davis business became increasingly international in scope during these years. In 1955, under the auspices of the International Cooperation Administration, the Firm was retained to assist the Ministry of Economics of the Pakistan Government in the development of a balanced and integrated program designed to stimulate industry in that country.

In carrying out this work, which was largely concerned with studies and reports, the Firm maintained a team of engineers in Pakistan for about three years, working in the country's fledgling textile, chemical, leather, and other industries. Camel cars were still the principal means of transporting freight in the country, which like many Asian and other foreign nations, needs modern transportation and power facilities before industry can function efficiently and reach the large mass markets that are essential for low-cost production.

Again under the auspices of the ICA, the Firm was retained by the Ministry of Mines and Petroleum of the Government of Bolivia, to survey the mining industry of the nation and develop a program for more efficient operation and expansion on the basis of available resources. On this project a team of engineers worked in Bolivia for more than two years, during a period of adverse economic conditions and severe unemployment. There was blood in the streets on more than one morning when the Ford, Bacon & Davis men went to work, and outbreaks of civil disorder lent urgency to the job of cutting costs and upgrading productivity in the nation's effort to improve its competitive position in world markets for tin and other natural resources.

Mr. Coldwell retired as president on January 1, 1957, and was succeeded by Mr. Whittelsey. In the 30-odd years since he had joined Ford, Bacon & Davis in 1925 as a young mining engineer,

Mr. Whittelsey had been responsible for progressively larger projects and had compiled a record for on-time completions within budgeted costs that was an important factor in his selection as the new president.

The spectacular economic progress which has been under way in Australia since World War II, marked by increasing industrialization of a one-time predominantly agricultral economy, has been further stimulated by discovery of oil and other minerals —coal, iron ore, copper, bauxite among them—in far larger quantities than needed for domestic consumption.

One of the major developments in this post-war boom is based on the copper-lead-zinc mining operations of Mount Isa Mines, Ltd. (52 per cent owned by American Smelting & Refining Company) at Mt. Isa, in north central Queensland, some 600 miles inland from the east coast at Townsville, which was the U.S. naval base during the Battle of the Coral Sea. The size of the ore reserves and world price trends indicated that a major expansion of the Mt. Isa properties would be feasible if economical transportation were available to move the substantial tonnages involved.

For this type of carriage, involving heavy bulk traffic over a period of years, the "steel wheel on a steel rail" is still by far the most efficient method of transportation, but the existing rail line of the Queensland Government Railways was completely inadequate for the purpose.

Early in 1957, the Government of Queensland, in cooperation with the Federal Government, decided to evaluate the economics of the situation, with a view to modernizing the property to handle proposed expansion of the mines. Ford, Bacon & Davis was retained by the Government to undertake a feasibility study covering Mount Isa's mineral reserves and the Company's plans for developing them, the estimated cost of modernizing the railroad to handle the heavier traffic, and projected revenues necessary to support the financing and operation of the line.

CHARLES C. WHITTELSEY
Director, 1946–1966
President, 1957–1965
Chairman, 1959–1966

In a study and report completed in November, 1957, FB&D staff personnel under Leander H. Poor as senior engineer, and Demetri G. Niarchos, civil engineer, found that the project was economically sound in relation to cost and projected revenue, and that the ore reserves at Mt. Isa were more than adequate for a long-range mining program at several times the former rate of production.

This report to the Queensland Government set an estimated cost of $65,000,000 for the necessary relocating, regrading, new track and bridge construction on 750 miles of line from Collinsville, via Townsville, to Mt. Isa. Collinsville is the source of coal for the Mt. Isa Mines power plant, which supports the mining operation and the community itself.

The report was favorably received but nearly two years were to pass before financing problems could be resolved by the Queensland Government. In October, 1959, the Australian Commonwealth Government announced that the equivalent of $45,000,000 would be made available to supplement $22,500,000 which had been authorized previously by the Queensland Government. Shortly afterward, Ford, Bacon & Davis was retained as agent to provide engineering services, and to manage an expanded rehabilitation program, which has come to be known as the Mt. Isa Railway project.

L. H. Poor, who was senior engineer on the feasibility work, served as senior supervisory engineer, with Ferdinand H. Dietze of the Monroe office as project manager, and Mr. Niarchos of the New York office as project engineer.

In retrospect, an unusual facet of the Mt. Isa project was the abrogation of a clause in the agreement under which FB&D made the feasibility report—that the firm consider itself ineligible for any work which resulted from the study. An ineligibility clause is not unusual in such work, since it frees the recommendations of any implication of bias or future self-interest.

Such a clause was, at the request of the Australian Government, included in the agreement for the Mt. Isa feasibility study.

Before the study was complete, however, the Government requested that FB&D cancel this proviso, and continue with the project as consultant and manager of construction. With understandable promptness, FB&D complied.

With the problem of financing the project resolved, Ford, Bacon & Davis established its own offices in Brisbane, which have served as Australian headquarters since that time.

Late in 1960, following months of intensive work, detailed engineering designs were submitted on the project, which was to continue into the following decade as one of the few large railroad construction jobs of modern times.

Other business was developing abroad at the time. A report was requested in 1957 by Olin Mathieson Corporation on the feasibility of a project to produce alumina from bauxite in French Guiana. A similar investigation was commissioned by Dillon, Read & Co., prominent investment bankers acting for Japanese interests weighing the economic factors in a proposed pulp and lumber project in Alaska.

In the same year a team of Ford, Bacon & Davis men departed for Bilbao, Spain, where under the direction of Lionel S. Baldin, they were busy for months on an engineering study of the operations of Spain's largest privately-owned steel mill—Altos Hornos de Vizcaya, S.A.

Although part of the engineering staff was widely dispersed over the world on these foreign assignments, a large group was equally busy on projects in the United States and Canada.

Construction work was being handled in large volume, and in 1957 it became desirable to provide larger facilities at the Monroe, La., headquarters of the construction subsidiary. These new buildings and shops had been needed for some time but deferred to meet pressing client commitments. For the men assigned to the work, it was, of course, a labor of love, since they were designing their own offices, drafting and other work-space.

The result was a carefully planned, highly efficient, yet comfortable and attractive grouping of air conditioned offices, drafting rooms, file and storage space, along with a cafeteria and patio for outdoor luncheons in suitable weather.

This suitable weather during 1957 was limited to brief periods between long spells of rain—and there is nothing worse for pipeliners than rain and mud, unless it is hurricanes. This year Ford, Bacon & Davis got both.

Hurricane Audrey struck the Louisiana coast at Cameron, where the firm was busy on a pipeline project then at a stage where a maximum amount of trenching, pipe and equipment were vulnerable to storm damage.

It was a catastrophe for the local residents, however, far worse than the damage to work under way and to job equipment. The Ford, Bacon & Davis crew turned first to rescue operations, and completed this urgent task before appraising their own losses.

These losses, among other things, included a brand new trailer job-office, and several days elapsed before it was even found, let alone repaired, cleaned up and moved back to the job site. The heavy machinery, pipe-handling equipment, trucks and other tools had been under salt water which flooded inland areas, and had to be completely overhauled and cleaned before work could be resumed.

Abnormal rainfall continued through 1957, seeming to concentrate on areas where pipeline work was under way, holding up the jobs and increasing costs despite every effort to regain lost time during spells of favorable weather.

The following year, 1958, was marked by a sharp curtailment in industry spending on new plant and equipment, with signs of overcapacity appearing in a number of areas. For the relatively small amount of engineering design work and construction that did become available, competition was unusually keen.

As in the past, the Firm's report and appraisal work continued as a source of profitable business, while Ford, Bacon & Davis Construction Corporation had a large program of pipeline work under way which carried through most of the year.

Dayton Power & Light required, in connection with a rate

case, an evaluation of its gas properties which the Firm was assigned to make.

An unusual and challenging job came in during the year, involving a study and report on the feasibility of a project to obtain iron ore from a deposit in New Quebec, north of Labrador, for Ungava Iron Ores Company. An investigation was required of potential markets for the ore in Europe, which were found to be very substantial.

As finally evolved, the project provided that the ore would be beneficiated in a plant at tidewater, before shipment to European and North American ports. Since shipments from Ungava Bay can be made only during four summer months each year, plans provided for a storage and transfer site on the ice-free southwest coast of Greenland, which makes possible regular year-around shipments to customers.

Business soon recovered from the slow-down of 1958, and the concluding years of the decade brought major assignments at opposite ends of the world.

Ford, Bacon & Davis engineers in 1960 were busy in Italy, in Spain, and in Australia, while a crew in Waco, Tex., was handling the right-of-way studies, engineering design and construction of a natural gas pipeline from the Old Ocean Field to steam generating stations in the Fort Worth area. Completed on a 20-month work schedule, the job under the original direction of George T. Dierking as project manager, involved some 375 miles of 16-inch to 24-inch pipe and ran into no delaying problems—which itself is unusual on any engineering project with a firm time-schedule.

The Firm marked its 65th anniversary in 1959 by moving into its present spacious offices in the new building at 2 Broadway, overlooking New York Harbor, and providing facilities on a single floor (the 21st) to house its by now large and important library and files, as well as drafting rooms, offices, conference rooms and other facilities.

Plans were under way for the new and larger quarters for the west coast office at 235 Montgomery Street, San Francisco, which is headed by John G. Lewis, Captain, U.S.N., retired, who joined the organization in 1959.

In Monroe, Ford, Bacon & Davis Construction Corporation, only recently installed in its new building, found it necessary to set up temporary drafting rooms in the shops to handle a heavy influx of pipeline work from Southern Natural Gas Company, the Michigan-Wisconsin Pipe Line Company, and Texas Gas Transmission Company, as well as assignments from the City of Monroe.

Late in 1959, on application of the trustee, a new appraisal was authorized of the railroad properties and operations of the bankrupt Hudson & Manhattan Railroad Company, which owns the rapid transit tubes under the Hudson River between Hoboken, Jersey City and New York.

The assignment required a current valuation of all railroad properties, giving effect to various possible future developments.

Operations were at a high level as the decade came to a close. With men at work in Spain and Australia, five field offices were handling construction in various parts of the United States, and another group was in Boston working on a plan to utilize historic Boston Common as an underground parking facility in an effort to relieve congestion in congested downtown streets.

In 1960 and 1961, the Firm was selected to design and supervise construction of a $6,000,000 wood shavings board plant for the Crossett Lumber Co., Crossett, Ark. With a capacity of 100 tons of finished product daily, the facility used gum wood and was the second of its type to be built by FB&D which utilizes the so-called Behr process. The first was built in 1955–1957 in Arcata, Calif., for Roddis Plywood Corporation, which licensed the process to Crossett.

Another Construction Corporation group was also close to home at this time, working on engineering and construction to modernize the West Monroe, La., plant of Olin Mathieson Chemical Corporation's Forest Products Division. The job consisted of added capacity for the pulp mill, modifying the facilities for more flexible operations, modernization of two paper machines, installation of a bark-burning boiler and of new materials handling equipment. Edwin C. Rowan was project engineer.

Bostonians have a deep attachment for the 48-acre park in the center of the city known as The Common, and plans for building a parking garage underneath it met with no enthusiasm until it became completely clear that the project would not disturb a blade of green grass, let alone the trees and gardens of the historic area. It was over 140 years old when the Revolution broke out in 1776, and Bostonians were determined that it remain untouched by the heavy hand of progress for at least as many centuries to come.

With assurances that only a corner of the tract, at Charles and Beacon Streets, would be required for entrance-exit ramps, the Massachusetts Parking Authority was able to forestall a public outcry. Ford, Bacon & Davis was assigned multiple responsibilities by the MPA, as the proposal gained support. The problem of downtown traffic congestion in the crowded old city had long been acute.

First came a feasibility study, covering costs and projected revenues, to support a $9,600,000 revenue bond issue. The bonds were sold and construction proceeded with Ford, Bacon & Davis as functional design engineer. On completion of the facility, which has a capacity of close to 1,500 cars, the Firm was retained as consulting engineers to make annual studies and reports on its operations.

In Boston, they tend to take the long view. An unusual aspect of this assignment is that it extends over the life of the bond issue or until the year 2,000, a 40-year period in which bondholders are assured of a watchful and impartial eye on the operations that service and will ultimately retire their securities.

At Ford, Bacon & Davis, 40 years is not an unusual span of individual employment. Younger staff engineers of today may well be active when this assignment is finally terminated with the maturity of the last outstanding bonds. The Firm will have marked its 100th anniversary six years before that.

Both the Firm and the Construction Corporation were involved at this time, in the latter's home town of Monroe, in a $5,000,000 civic improvement program which included extensions and modernization of the city's storm drainage and sanitary sewer system. The Firm prepared the preliminary report on which a bond issue was sold to finance the program. The largest single project was a large, concrete lined storm drainage canal traversing the entire city. Much of the 40-year old sanitary system was badly deteriorated. The old concrete pipe was lined with corrugated metal pipe, which was threaded into place, thus in effect creating a new system at minimum cost.

A large project for Milwaukee Gas Light Co., consisting of two large Service Centers on the North and South sides of the city, represented a not unusual problem when test-borings showed that the site for one of them was on unstable soil, requiring some 1,200 concrete piles to be poured in steel shells driven 50 to 70 feet down in order to provide a solid foundation for the 112,000 square-foot building. The project, on which Ford, Bacon & Davis did the design engineering and supervised construction, was completed on schedule.

Construction of approximately 1,000 miles of pipe line ranging from 30 down to 4 inches, got under way in March, 1960, for Michigan Wisconsin Pipe Line Company, under the supervision of the late Monroe S. Trimble as project manager. Mr. Trimble, a graduate of Louisiana Polytechnical Institute, had supervised all pipe line work for this client since 1955.

Most of the job consisted of loop lines from Meade, Kans., to northern Wisconsin, which included 343 miles of 24-inch line from Meade to Sandwich, Ill., 192 miles of 30-inch line from Sandwich to Woolfolk Station and 26 miles of smaller line in Wisconsin from Little Chute to De Pere. In addition, as part of the company's 1960 program, approximately 300 miles were built of 24- and 20-inch main line, with 16- to 4-inch laterals and another 150 miles of small lateral lines connecting cities in Missouri, Iowa and Wisconsin.

At Falls Church, Va., another field office was managing work for the Chesapeake & Potomac Telephone Company. This project consisted of locating, surveying, mapping, right-of-way acquisition, and preparation of engineering construction drawings for 80 miles of underground telephone cable.

Since in the nature of things, engineering and construction work comes in cycles, it is desirable for a large organization like Ford, Bacon & Davis to develop services which are in more or less continuing demand.

Appraisals, valuations and reports of various types have provided this type of work over the years, and provided an unusual degree of stability for an organization of this type.

Another service of this nature was developed in the spring of 1959, based on the Firm's close relations with the pipe line industry as designer and builder of thousands of miles of such carriers. This was a pipe sealing service which, using a patented sealant under pressure, can eliminate the need for excavating to repair leaky mains. A preparation called Con-Seal, and the patented "Never-Leak" method are used under a licensing arrangement with Consolidated Edison of New York.

After careful analyses based on experience with the method, Ford, Bacon and Davis engineers discovered that the idea has value far beyond that of eliminating leaks. It can also be used to upgrade low-pressure mains to handle pressures up to four times that for which they were designed, thus sharply increasing the capacity of a local or regional distribution system at very little additional cost.

The system also eliminates clogging of valves and meters that frequently follows older sealing methods, which leave residues of jute, rust and powdered tar in the pipe.

The Never-Leak system uses a solution of fine, rubber-like particles in a water solution that dries quickly and self-cures to form a tough, resilient lining which penetrates into the smallest cracks, and bonds to the pipe as a permanent inner coating.

Using special equipment which includes tank pumper trucks, the system provides a valuable maintenance service to gas companies. Because the sealant dries and cures rapidly, it can be used with only a brief shut-down of gas service to customers during a few off-peak hours, usually late at night.

Feasibility studies to support financing for expansion were also made in 1960, for the City of Eugene, Ore., and for Harvey Aluminum, Inc. Some $40,000,000 of new securities was involved, $25,000,000 to expand the electric power facilities in Eugene, and $15,000,000 for a proposed plant expansion for Harvey Aluminum.

In Lexington, Ky., the Firm was engaged in an appraisal of the Lexington Water Co., properties, originally built in 1890 and supplying some 30,000 people. Under the original franchise the city had the right to purchase the system at a fair current price, based on impartial appraisals.

In Columbus, Ohio, another group was sifting facts as "umpire" in a dispute between the city and citizen groups over a proposed increase in the local transit fare. Another project was a study made for the State of Kentucky, on its advantages as a site for primary aluminum plants and processing facilities, which sparked an effort by the Department of Economic Development to bring this type of industry into the state.

In the 20 years since 1940 alone, something over $2,000,000,-000 of design and construction of industrial, utility, pipeline, railroad and other facilities had been completed by Ford, Bacon & Davis, Inc., and Ford, Bacon & Davis Construction Corporation, excluding the huge volume of other professional engineering services provided for clients in the two decades.

VIII

Low-Cost Production: 'Secret Weapon' in American Triumph over Poverty

IN THE DECADES since 1894, when two young engineers formed a partnership under the name of Ford & Bacon, the United States has become by far the biggest and the most successful "aggressor nation" in history.

This aggression, however, has not been directed at other peoples, but at the forces of nature which refuse to feed, clothe and shelter mankind unless made to do so by human effort.

The American conquest of the human condition, creating abundance for a nation that will soon number 200,000,000 people, has been primarily the job of engineers, whether or not earlier practitioners called themselves that. It was almost exactly a century before the founding of Ford, Bacon & Davis that Eli Whitney, on March 14, 1794, obtained a patent on his cotton engine—usually contracted to "gin"—and went on to establish, in the manufacture of guns, the principle of high precision that is basic in all mass production.

Whitney and other leaders of the long U.S. war on poverty called themselves inventors and businessmen, which they were. But they were also engineers, by instinct and ability if not by academic training, shaping a wilderness into an engine of production that is today the largest and most efficient in the world.

The incredible size of the economic structure which American businessmen and engineers have built in the decades since Ford, Bacon & Davis was founded is evident in the Department of Commerce figures on gross national product in 1965—some $676 billion, and an increase of $47 billion over 1964.

The increase alone was roughly equal to the total GNP of thriving Canada, and about half the total GNP of France or Great Britain. Even the American percentage gain, at 5.5%, was topped only by two relatively small nations.

The first half of the decade of the 1960's was a period of almost uninterrupted world expansion, in which inflationary trends and solid economic growth seemed to have formed a close working partnership.

In the United States, commercial bank loans and investments, supported by Federal Reserve policies, rose steadily at better than an 8% annual rate, creating a huge increase in the supply of money. And the gross national product, measured in constant dollars to eliminate the impact of rising prices, increased some $30 billion a year on the average—a total of nearly $150 billion in the five-year period.

Per capita income after taxes was up by a fifth, and the massive U.S. economy, creating new jobs at the rate of 1,200,000 a year, put an additional 6,000,000 people to work. Official figures showed "unemployment" down to 4% of the statistical "work force," which as most personnel managers agree, is close to the bottom of the barrel so far as employables are concerned —dependable people who are willing and able to turn in a good day's work for a day's pay.

In most other countries of the Free World, the story was much the same. Business and industry were pushing ahead. Prosperity was in many cases further stimulated by development of natural resources either newly-discovered, or dormant in the past for lack of capital and enterprise.

By 1961, work was well under way on the Mt. Isa Railway Project, with various phases of the job handled by Australian and U.S. contracting firms working from FB&D plans and specifications and under FB&D supervision as agent for the Queensland Government.

The undertaking involved relaying nearly 250 miles with heavier rail, some 215 miles of complete relocation and new track construction, the building of nearly 150 bridges in addition to the big, new 2,400-foot through truss bridge over the Burdekin River at Macrossan. Like the rest of the modernized line, it is designed for an axle-load of 16.8 tons, about three times that of the older structure it replaced.

New and heavier rail was laid in 120-foot welded lengths. Substantial construction economies were effected by using standard 30- and 45-foot pre-stressed concrete spans for the new bridges, which were placed well above normal flood level.

Following a further FB&D report on operations of the Queensland Railways, the work of FB&D's Brisbane office was expanded in 1962 to develop effective administrative systems for reporting and controlling operations of the entire Northern Division of the Government-owned railway system.

To provide adequate office space for operating the modernized system, an administration building for the Railways was designed and built at Townsville.

The job involved not only larger offices, but a staff of clerical and supervisory personnel, and installation of IBM data processing equipment. Information on some 6,000 rules of standard practice was collected, processed and organized into systems and methods of reporting on all operations, with descriptions and functions of 257 key supervisory jobs.

At the dedication of the new railroad administration building

Among the few major railroad construction jobs of recent years was the rebuilding of Australia's Mt. Isa line in Queensland at a cost of $60,000,000. A work train brings supplies for the new Macrossan Bridge replacing an old wooden trestle.

The Inlander, crack passenger train on the new Mt. Isa line, in Queensland, Australia, crosses the new Cloncurry River Bridge west of Cloncurry, cutting many hours from the time required for the run between Mt. Isa and the coast.

in Townsville, late in 1965, came an announcement from the Hon. Gordon W. W. Chalk, then Queensland Minister for Transport (now Treasurer and Deputy Premier), under whom FB&D had worked on the project, that the total cost would finally come in at 10% below the original budget, a saving on the order of $6,000,000. Over the completely modernized line, a crack passenger train, the Inlander, is running on the fastest schedule of any train in the state, cutting 25 to 50% from previous time over its 600-mile route.

Late in 1964, with the Mt. Isa–Townsville job nearing completion, Ford, Bacon & Davis was awarded a contract for a somewhat smaller but highly important railroad construction job about 300 miles south of the Mt. Isa project.

This assignment, now known as the Moura Project, grew out of a feasibility report submitted to the Queensland Railways in 1964, following studies made by L. H. Poor, who had succeeded Mr. Dietze as project manager on the Mt. Isa Project in 1963. The FB&D responsibilities on the Moura Project were the same as those for the Mt. Isa railroad job—design, supervision of engineering and management of construction.

Coal deposits at Moura, about 110 miles from the east coast at Gladstone, had been developed. The plan is to supply some 29.6 million tons of coking coal to Japan by a group, formed for the purpose, of Australian, American and Japanese interests—Thiess-Peabody-Mitsui, Ltd. The deliveries will run over a 13-year period from early 1965. The existing line of the Queensland Railways wound for 200 miles from Moura to Gladstone via Rockhampton, and was inadequate and inefficient for the haulage of large tonnages of coal.

Based on surveys that established a new "short line" route direct from the mines to the coast at Gladstone, Ford, Bacon & Davis estimated the cost of the project at $22.5 million, not including the 36 locomotives and 200 hopper cars required to move the tonnage involved.

Like the Mt. Isa line, the Moura project is a 3-foot 6-inch gauge (compared with the British–U.S. standard of 4 feet 8½ inches) but the road-bed, bridges and other structures have been designed for the wider gauge so that a change-over can be made at minimum cost, if traffic in future years requires it.

The design of the Moura road is for a single track with ruling grades of 1.5% eastbound, and 2% westbound, with passing loops at suitable intervals for uninterrupted movement of 60-car trains which will haul out the coal at an initial rate of 3 million tons a year, expandable to 5 million tons by 1970. The project, managed for Ford, Bacon & Davis by Demetri G. Niarchos, who had been project engineer and assistant project manager on the Mt. Isa job, includes modern terminal facilities designed to handle expanding traffic requirements.

Queensland, with almost exactly two and a half times the area of Texas, but with less than a sixth of the population, anticipates far-reaching benefits from the two railroads tying inland areas with the coast and making possible fast, dependable transportation for all types of freight as economic activity gains increasing momentum over future years.

Harsh proof of Australia's wisdom in seeking to diversify a huge farm economy by development of natural resources and increased industrial activity came in 1965, when a devastating drought in many sections of the country cut farm income by more than $200 million, and caused heavy losses of livestock. With a further loss estimated at $400 million in the 1965–66 season, the drought provided fresh stimulus to the nation's resource development program, aimed to cut down import requirements and bring the country's international payments situation into better balance.

The Firm's overseas assignments continued to increase through the 1960's. By early 1963, a wide range of important assignments had taken FB&D engineers to more than 30 nations on every continent.

[172]

For Canadian Fina Oil Ltd., of Calgary, Alberta, a report was made on the extraction, processing and transportation of crude oil from the Athabasca tar sands development, a huge deposit in which the petroleum requires special extractive methods.

At the same time a team was in Ceylon, appraising marketing properties of an Esso Standard subsidiary to support a claim arising from Government expropriation of these and other foreign holdings in the country.

For Interfinancial Corporation, a study and report was made as a basis for developing and financing a proposed limestone quarry in the Province of Chubut, Argentina. Another project was under way in Latin America, preparing specifications for the Panama Canal Company (owned by the U.S. Government) for new equipment. The job included engineering and design services on an expansion of electric generating capacity, as well as additional transmission and distribution facilities.

Accurate, up-to-date information on world production and markets is obviously a highly important management tool in planning for future growth. In 1961, an international survey was undertaken for Asbestos Corp., Ltd., of Montreal, which covered Europe, including Iron Curtain countries, Japan, Australia, India and Israel. Data were compiled to indicate available supply in various markets, and potential future demand in these and other world markets.

The assignment took FB&D behind the Iron Curtain into Poland, East Germany, Czecho-Slovakia, Hungary and Yugo-Slavia. Robert D. Kirk, working on the survey, found himself on a bus in Czecho-Slovakia without the proper currency to pay his fare. Dollars, pounds, francs and marks were refused by the conductor. A fellow-passenger came to his rescue and insisted on paying for him. On arrival in Prague, the doorman at the hotel where he planned to stay, supplied currency for the cab fare. Unlike the stranger on the bus, the doorman happily accepted reimbursement later, along with a suitable "commission."

While in East Berlin, Kirk was subjected to intensive political indoctrination from a Government official less concerned with asbestos purchases than with alleged Western hostility to the Communist regime. He was finally able to convince the Communist official that his interest in asbestos overshadowed every other consideration, political and otherwise, and thus turned the interview into commercial channels. But only after an extended lecture on the evils of capitalism and private property.

The 1961 asbestos assignment had a somewhat unusual, although not unique, sequel. In 1964, a different client requested a current survey of the same international scope. The initial work would, of course, provide a valuable background except that it was the property of Asbestos Corp., Ltd., of Montreal.

Informed of the situation, Asbestos Corp. agreed to the release of its 1961 data for the purpose, provided it be given a copy of the new report. This was agreeable to Lake Asbestos of Quebec, Ltd., the new client. Both clients thus obtained valuable marketing and other information at a lower cost than would otherwise have been possible.

The Ford, Bacon & Davis organization has had long and varied experience in the cement industry, and has studied and reported on a number of large and highly-efficient plants in several sections of the country.

In 1960 came an important assignment on a joint venture of Cerro Corporation and Newmont Mining Company, involving the organization of Atlantic Cement Co., to embark on an entirely new concept in production and distribution. It involved construction of a large, low-cost producing facility which would use cheap water transportation to supply a major seaboard market from Boston to Miami. Transportation costs normally limit cement distribution to a distance of a few hundred miles.

FB&D was assigned to make a feasibility study, which determined that a large facility, on the order of 10,000,000 barrels annual capacity, and fully automated to hold down costs, would be competitive along the entire eastern seaboard.

On completion of the report, FB&D handled other assignments for Atlantic Cement, including inspection of the new plant, and furnishing an engineering certificate to the trustees for the bonds issued to finance the plant.

In Australia, a market study was made for National Castings Company, covering cargo containers, Speedloader equipment, cast steel grinding balls and other products.

Spain has made impressive economic progress in recent years and the nation's largest steel producer—Altos Hornos de Vizcaya, S.A., with mills at Bilbao and Valencia—has shared fully in this growth. For several years, starting in 1957, FB&D engineers worked with Spain's "Big Steel"—consulting and furnishing engineering services in a long-range program to upgrade mill facilities, processes and methods in order to help maintain the company's competitive position and enable it to meet a steadily-increasing demand for steel.

A comprehensive pre-investment survey of Turkey's metalworking, chemical and fertilizer industries was commissioned by the U.S. Agency for International Development early in 1962. Similar to other studies by FB&D in post-war years, it furnished the basis for an evaluation of investment opportunities for Turkish and other investors. A team of eight engineers and other experts spent weeks in Turkey surveying existing facilities, raw material resources and markets, in order to determine priorities for expansion in the over-all development program.

The spring of 1962 found FB&D engineers at work in Chile, estimating construction costs in connection with the financing of a huge copper mining and ore processing project. Louis C. Raymond and Charles G. Schneider headed the FB&D team. A smaller group was in Mexico seeking data for a proposed manufacturing plant to produce mud pumps for the petroleum industry. Another group was in Israel, in connection with the engineering, design and construction of a carbon black plant.

The Chilean project, undertaken for Cerro Corporation, involved a study of facilities that would stretch from an ore body

[175]

high in the Andes Mountains, on the Argentine border, to the Pacific Coast. Because of heavy snowfall and rugged terrain, the ore travels down through more than three miles of tunnels from the mining operations to the separation mill.

Diversification is neither a U.S. invention nor an American monopoly. European companies have been at it for years, and in some cases have carried it out just as successfully.

Verolme United Shipyards of Rotterdam is an example. The company operates three shipyards in Holland, with similar operations in Ireland, Norway and Brazil, plus another and new yard in Mexico. It also manufactures engines, boilers, electrical equipment and high vacuum metallizing machines.

These metallizing machines, built at a plant in Weisbaden, West Germany, were the basis for an FB&D assignment, in 1963, to determine potential markets for metallized fabrics, plastic film and paper in the U.S. The end products are such varied articles as metallized cellulose for bandages, plastic Christmas trees, and synthetic fabrics for window drapes and curtains.

It was a busy year at home, too. For Revere Copper & Brass Company, a plant location study was made covering a proposed 60,000 ton-a-year aluminum rolling mill.

Later, Revere revised its plans, deciding to locate farther south and to increase the capacity of the new facility by 50%, and selected a new site at Scottsboro, Ala., where community financing was available.

In this connection, Ford, Bacon & Davis was retained in 1965 to make a feasibility study to support an industrial revenue bond issue for $55,000,000 in connection with the project. At the time, it was the largest financing of this type ever undertaken. The new site also provides for a reduction plant in the future.

Over the years, the FB&D construction subsidiary has performed numerous jobs for its home city of Monroe, La. Having the needed staff already on location, it has been able to provide a superior result at minimum cost, and to help keep the municipal facilities at a high level of operating efficiency.

Close cooperation of municipal officials was a vital factor in obtaining these results, particularly of the mayor and the general manager of the Utilities Commission which administers the city-owned electric service.

For example, in early 1962, the nation's largest combined cycle power generation unit was placed in operation for the City of Monroe Utilities Commission. The work had started back in 1957–58, when a gas turbine was installed under FB&D supervision, as a first step in a plan which called for later installation of a steam generating unit.

The second step was completed and synchronized into the system in 1961, giving the city an installed capacity of 66,500 kilowatts. The combined cycle feature stems from utilization of the hot exhaust gases from the 10,000 kw gas turbine which in turn provides steam through a waste-heat boiler for a conventional 22,000 kw turbine generator.

The net result is a 10% fuel saving and a very high degree of efficiency for power generation in the city. The $4,000,000 project included installation of an alternate fuel system to use either natural gas or, on a standby basis, fuel oil.

In mid-1962, FB&D headed a group of companies which bid successfully for a National Aeronautics and Space Administration contract.

The job, initially, was the preparation of design criteria for the giant new flight acceleration test facility at the NASA Manned Spacecraft Center in Houston. Working with FB&D on the assignment were McKiernan-Terry Corporation, a subsidiary of Litton Industries, Inc., the Raytheon Company, Franklin Institute and the Cornell Aeronautical Laboratory, Inc. Following acceptance by NASA of these design criteria, the Firm and its associates were commissioned by the Army Corps of Engineers to prepare performance specifications for equipment. FB&D also prepared construction drawings and specifications for the building.

The facility, which includes a huge rotunda housing a centrifuge capable of whirling a simulated command module and its three-man crew at many times the normal force of gravity, involved a cost of something over $10,000,000. The accelerator requires nearly 7,000 HP equivalent to accelerate a 50-foot boom which carries a 3,000-pound payload, and provides an onset rate of 3G's per second.

A major modernization program at the West Allis, Wis., plant of Allis Chalmers was assigned to Ford, Bacon & Davis when the company decided late in 1962 to phase out its steam turbine generator operations. STG production had in some years accounted for 33% of direct labor manhours, and occupied some 600,000 square feet of space scattered through the 2,000,000 square foot plant.

The decision affected all production, and as part of the phase-out, a $50,000,000 backlog of orders had to be produced and delivered to customers. The client formed a 28-man team of engineers from its manufacturing and sales departments and retained FB&D as consultants for engineering service and method guidelines.

Working closely together, this group devised an overall plan, based on the so-called "spare bedroom" principle, in which a complete change-over was made without interrupting necessary production in any phase of the complex operation. The job, which included a realignment of the shop supervision set-up as well as rearrangement of facilities, achieved a 25% reduction in the production cycle. The initial installation of a computer-controlled scheduling of all operations, from design to shipping, was a key phase of the assignment.

The record shows that Ford, Bacon & Davis has so far designed, built, managed and made engineering, economic and feasibility studies on pipeline systems that in the aggregate run approximately 60,000 miles and represent a total investment of several billion dollars. More than 115 clients in the oil and gas industries have entrusted major pipeline jobs to the Firm, and pipelining continues, as in the past, to be an important phase of FB&D's over-all operations.

In 1962, FB&D built some 262 miles of line ranging in diameter from 4½ to 20 inches, including gathering lines and meter runs, for American Natural Gas Company in Oklahoma and Wisconsin, at a cost of approximately $9,500,000.

The following year, a number of other sizeable pipeline projects were on the books. For Southern Natural Gas, a client of many years' standing for whom many millions of dollars has been expended, a Mississippi River crossing between Louisiana and Mississippi was built at a cost of $2,500,000.

In the same year, FB&D did preliminary surveying and mapping, acquisition of rights of way and settlement of damage claims on some 825 miles of the huge $350,000,000 Colonial Pipeline Company line to move petroleum products 1,600 miles from Houston to Linden, N.J. This 30- to 36-inch line has a capacity of 34 million gallons a day which can be boosted to 42 million with additional pumping stations.

Also, in 1963, the Firm built a 115-mile 12-inch petroleum products line from Pascagoula to Collins, Miss., where it joined the 800-mile Plantation Pipe Line Company line from Baton Rouge to Greensboro, N.C. FB&D had planned and constructed the Plantation line for Standard Oil of New Jersey during World War II. Cost of the new project was $4,500,000.

Another project during 1963 was an 87-mile complex of distribution systems serving 15 communities in Wisconsin, built for American Gas Company of Wisconsin. FB&D prepared technical and feasibility studies, testified before state and Federal authorities, prepared the engineering drawings and supervised construction of the project.

By this time, the volume of work moving through the organization had reached a point at which an internal data processing system was needed to take over jobs that had previously been handled by renting time at commercially available DP centers. A new IBM 1620 system was installed at the New York offices, consisting of six units which not only handle work previously processed at time-rental processing centers, but make economically possible a wide range of valuable services to clients in a fraction of the time otherwise required.

With a number of staff engineers already experts on the potentials and technology of data processing, the new installation was soon loaded with projects which either accelerated client assignments or broadened the scope of analyses and reports, in most cases both.

The extraordinary range of FB&D capabilities is evident in a list of some of the less spectacular assignments which flowed through the organization in the early 1960's: Updating a feasibility report for financing a newsprint mill in western Canada; consulting on structural and operational problems of the Rio Grande Gateway Bridge at Brownsville, Tex., when it was acquired from private interests by the Cameron County government; reviewing and analyzing electrical equipment purchases by a state government; determining relative packaging costs for a brewery, as between 16-ounce cans and one-way bottles; studying and reporting on the ready-mix cement industry in a large eastern metropolitan area, and estimating fair value of several midwest gas distributing systems.

For Ford, Bacon & Davis, the 1960's also saw completion of a number of important jobs that had been under study for some time. For the Homelite Division of Textron, a new plant was completed at Gastonia, N.C., in 1961, which grew out of an earlier study by the Valuation, Report and Industrial Department under Vice-President Lionel S. Baldin. Crowded conditions and labor costs at the former Homelite factory location led to a recommendation that the operation be moved into a new and more efficient plant at another location.

This in turn led to a study of potential sites, to design of a suitable building and to inspection of construction on behalf of the client, while the plant was being built. Homelite makes gasoline powered chain saws and small gasoline engines for various other purposes, including generation of electric power.

Defense activity was a major segment of the U.S. economy through these years. While the need for this continuing, and costly, program was widely deplored, there are hidden benefits from such activity that are frequently overlooked. Much of the research, development, and production technology evolved in meeting requirements and specifications for defense requirements, as engineers have found, have almost immediate application in commercial operations. While defense may well be a costly way to obtain these benefits, they are nevertheless a valuable stimulus to technological advances in many industrial areas —electronics, aviation, and atomic energy, for prime examples.

In mid-1964, Ford, Bacon & Davis received a contract to appraise the performance of the contractor responsible for maintenance and servicing of the Atomic Energy Commission's facilities at Los Alamos, N.M. Measured against accepted industrial standards, the adequacy and effectiveness of the operations was found to be fully in line with such standards, although certain improvements and economies were recommended.

In the fall of the same year, the Firm was awarded a contract by Langley Research Center, National Aeronautics and Space Administration, for design and engineering on a high pressure air compressor facility to be located at the Langley Center in Hampton, Va. A unique feature of the project was a test facility capable of delivering air at 6,000 cubic feet per minute at pressures in excess of 6,000 pounds per square inch.

By 1964, New England had long since recovered from the loss of its cotton textile industry to the South, and was sharing in the economic boom that steadily pushed U.S. economic indices to unprecedented levels. This was particularly true in Connecticut, where textiles had never been as important to the state's economy as they were to Massachusetts, Rhode Island or New Hampshire.

Emhart Corporation of Hartford, a highly diversified industrial complex with plants in the U.S. and Europe, found itself with obsolete and inadequate facilities for its big New Britain Division, the former American Hardware Corp. This division has long been a major producer of architectural locks and hardware (Russwin and Corbin) and other types of locks (Sesame and Kwikset) and, among other things, a patented automotive hose clamp used on engine cooling systems.

Growth projections for the business indicated the need for more space. The problem was whether to expand existing facilities in New Britain, either in conjunction with an urban renewal project or independently, or to find a new site close to the city and build an entirely new facility.

Ford, Bacon & Davis was retained to make the facility planning studies essential for a sound decision on the economics of the problem. This was completed early in 1965. The findings indicated substantial long-range advantages from sale of the old buildings, and removal of the operation into a suburb close enough to the former site so that the Company's trained and highly-skilled employees, a valuable asset, would be retained.

The FB&D study showed that despite a substantial cost differential, the benefits to be derived more than justified the expenditure. More important, there would be adequate provision for further low-cost expansion in future years.

The recommendations were accepted and FB&D retained as engineering consultant for detailed planning and concurrent engineering design and supervision of construction of a new plant, foundry and general offices in nearby Berlin, a few miles from the old site.

The new facilities provided some 778,400 square feet of space arranged for maximum operating efficiency, with much new production machinery and equipment.

Across the continent, at this time, the Firm was also busy as consulting engineer to the Department of Lighting of the City of

Seattle on the $85,000,000 Boundary Project to add 600,000 kilowatts to the city's electric utility system. Designed for an ultimate capacity of 900,000 kw, the project consists of a dam and power plant on the Pend Oreille River near the Canadian border. The project, as originally approved by the Federal Power Commission in 1961, was to cost $135,000,000. Continued refinement of plans, plus elimination of transmission costs through joint use of Bonneville Power Administration facilities, later cut the projected cost by $50,000,000. Completion of the undertaking was scheduled for 1967.

The resources of both FB&D and the Construction Corporation were combined to build the finishing section of a multimillion dollar titanium dioxide plant at Savannah, Ga., for American Cyanamid Company, toward the end of 1964. Under the close supervision of the client's own engineers, the two organizations worked closely on the design, engineering, purchase of equipment, and actual construction of the new facility. The assignment, a so-called turn-key job, included initial purchases of raw materials, start-up of the plant, and preliminary training of operating personnel.

From an engineering standpoint, preliminary studies of pipe line feasibility, applications to public authorities for certificates of public convenience, the route survey, acquisition of rights of way, and actual construction of the line are only part of the task. Pumping capacity, storage, potential markets and distribution are coordinate parts of the over-all job.

The central economic factor is the tariff—what revenue must be assured from realistic market projections, that will support the investment and provide an adequate payout over the assumed life of the facility.

This was the problem in early 1965, when FB&D was assigned by the Algerian Government to make tariff studies on its new "SONATRACH" project to bring crude oil north some 500 miles to the Mediterranean coast from Haoud el Hamra. SONA-

RUSSELL P. WESTERHOFF
Director, 1951–
President, 1965–
Chairman, 1966–

TRACH is a convenient acronym for Societe Nationale de Transport et de Commercialisation des Hydrocarbures.

The study included a re-check of planned capacity which showed that the line as designed would, in fact, carry the quantities projected. In extremely hot climates, there is a serious loss of power in pumping station turbines which can affect throughput as compared with norms based on temperate climates. The SONATRACH study showed that, on an annual basis which included high efficiency in the cooler months, the flow would be fully up to specifications.

In mid-1965, Mr. Westerhoff was elected president of Ford, Bacon & Davis to succeed Mr. Whittelsey, who continued as chairman of the board and chief executive officer. Mr. Westerhoff had moved up through the valuation and engineering departments to become assistant manager of the construction department and, in 1950, manager of the engineering department. The following year he was named a director and vice-president, engineering, of the Company. He was made vice-president and chief engineer in 1959, and vice-president, operations, in 1961, having meantime become a vice-president and director of the Construction Corporation as well.

Work was nearing completion in 1965 on Pittsburgh's $60,-000,000 Allegheny Center, a huge urban development project in which central air-conditioning as well as heating is made available to a complex of some 1,570 apartments and town houses, as well as 800,000 square feet of commercial space, including a large enclosed shopping mall and a theater.

The $4,000,000 central heating and air-conditioning plant, conceived and owned by an Equitable Gas Company subsidiary, was designed by Ford, Bacon & Davis, and built under FB&D supervision. It supplies the Center through a network of some 4.5 miles of underground insulated pipes which honeycomb the 79-acre site, providing hot water as well as heat and air-conditioning to every unit in the Center. Use of the service is metered to individual tenants, and is under tenant control through individual regulators in each store, office or home, with cost based on individual usage.

The gas-powered central system is believed to represent a major advance in efficiency and economy that is widely adaptable to urban and suburban developments of this type. Allegheny Center, sponsored by a group headed by Aluminum Corporation of America, stands on the north side of the Allegheny River, across from Pittsburgh's famed Golden Triangle, and is a further step in the spectacular redevelopment of this key industrial area that has attracted nationwide interest.

The decision of the Supreme Court, New York County, late in 1965, awarding the Hudson & Manhattan Corporation a total of nearly $73,000,000 for the railroad, tunnels and other property, was based to a great extent on a valuation report by Ford, Bacon & Davis. FB&D had been retained for the study after the properties were taken over in condemnation proceedings by the Port of New York Authority's railroad operating subsidiary, the Port Authority Trans-Hudson Corporation (PATH).

Four pages of the Court decision were devoted to outlining the methods used by Ford, Bacon & Davis in developing reproduction cost of the properties "in order that credence may be given to the accuracy of their findings and estimates" and "uncontroverted expert evidence."

The figure, which the Court pointed out had been "reconstructed from an exhaustive search for and analysis of original records," was $448,000,000. PATH attorneys claimed that, since the properties operated at a loss, they were worth only their value as salvage, which would be about $1,000,000.

Of the $73,000,000 total, about $18,000,000 was for the two office buildings at 30 and 50 Church Street, New York, and the balance of $55,000,000 for the railroad properties. PATH had taken over the properties September 1, 1962, by condemnation, continuing to provide service from midtown and downtown

Manhattan to Hoboken, Jersey City and the Pennsylvania Railroad station in Newark, via the Hudson River tubes.

The court proceedings, to determine the amount to be paid for the properties, ended in May, 1965, after about six months of controversial testimony.

Ford, Bacon & Davis developed for the railroad evidence to show both reproduction cost less depreciation, and original cost based on an analysis of old records. This was found to be about $62,000,000, and trended to September 1, 1962, came to $448,-000,000 after depreciation.

Todd Shipyards Corporation was one of several involved in 1966 in the Department of Defense "Fast Deployment Logistic Ship Project"—a program combining air transport to move troops to any part of the world on an emergency basis with fast, specially-designed ships to maintain necessary supply lines in support of such operations.

Initially some 20 to 40 vessels, specially designed for this logistical support, will be built at a cost of around $1 billion. Todd retained FB&D as consultant on project management and systems analysis, as well as for the conceptual design of a new shipbuilding facility to handle its construction work under the Defense Department program.

Whatever the readjustments that may lie ahead, the first half of the decade of the 1960's drew to a close in a period of unprecedented economic growth among the nations of the West, and the huge U.S. economy was setting the pace—and in not a few areas was actually widening its margin of leadership.

This leadership goes back half a century, and these years have seen a spectacular speed-up in engineering progress in the planning and building of low-cost industrial plants, efficient electric and gas power systems, communications and transportation facilities and other productive structures that make it possible for Americans today to live far better on 40 hours of work a week than their grandparents lived by working more than twice as hard and nearly twice as long.

Statistical evidence of this achievement can be found in dozens of industries, many of which came into existence in a period when machines and the energy to run them were taking over substantially all the hard, monotonous effort required to maintain a standard of living that has rightly been called the envy of the world.

Perhaps nowhere is the dominant economic position of the United States more clearly evident than in the electric power industry where Ford, Bacon & Davis got its start back in Philadelphia over 70 years ago.

At the end of 1965, installed generating capacity in the United States reached 253,000,000 kilowatts. In 1902, when initial records were compiled, it was less than 3,000,000 kw. On the basis of orders placed and construction under way, the total will reach 268,000,000 kw at the end of 1966, and is almost equal to that of the next five power-producing nations combined —Russia, Britain, Japan, West Germany and Canada. (Red China has a slightly larger capacity than Sweden.) From these facilities, the United States produces and consumes nearly as much power a year as the next six nations put together.

The growth of the electric power industry is, of course, only one phase of the huge increase in energy consumption that has occurred in America in the last 40 years and more. In a period when population increased 80%, energy consumption has increased three times as fast.

In 1920, total use of energy (in trillions of Btu's) was less than 20,000. In 1965, it was well over 50,000, and close to a third of the world total.

Because for more than a century steel has been a vital component in an industrial economy, few facts describe more succinctly what has happened than the tonnage output of the industry.

In 1894, aggregate production of steel in the 34 years since the industry began to keep records in 1860, had reached less than

53,000,000 tons. By 1926, only 32 years later, this was a single year's output. In 1965, with production at an all-time peak of 131,185,000 tons, it represented less than five months' ingot tonnage.

Because it was believed to be misleading, compilation of steel output in the United States, as a per cent of ingot capacity, was discontinued by the American Iron & Steel Institute back in 1960 and since then there has been no official measurement of "capacity." The last figure published by the AISI in 1960 was 148,570,970 tons a year. If the same measurement were still in use, it is probable that it would be on the order of 200,000,000 tons. Much of this would be high cost production from obsolete facilities, but it is nevertheless the astounding total of ingot that, under war or other pressure, the industry could pour if cost were no consideration. The highest comparable figure so far claimed by Russia is around 60,000,000 tons.

Early in 1966, the AISI announced that its 106-year cumulative total had passed 4 billion tons. By mid-1966, in other words, the industry had produced this huge aggregate during the years since Ford, Bacon & Davis was founded.

And no insignificant portion of it Ford, Bacon & Davis has helped put in place—in trolley lines, electric power plants, industrial facilities of every description and in a network of thousands of miles of pipeline which carry gas and oil to major population centers from coast to coast.

The U.S. pipeline network by 1965 had reached a total of some 756,000 miles of which over 200,000 miles were cross-country transmission lines, nearly two and a half times the mileage in service 20 years ago. The gas utility and pipeline industry, which Ford, Bacon & Davis had served almost from its inception, had revenues in 1965 of more than $11 billion, compared with less than $1.4 billion in 1945.

In 1965, another major consumer of steel, the automobile industry, produced no less than 11,137,364 cars, buses and trucks—well over 30,000 a day—valued at more than $20 billion. It brought the industry's aggregate since 1900, when it produced 4,192 cars, to upwards of 200 million vehicles, of which about 90 million are still in service.

Transportation and communications have kept pace with industrial expansion. Around 90 million telephones were in service in the United States at the end of 1965, nearly as many as in the rest of the world put together.

Despite the fact that there were over 15 million trucks and buses on the nation's 2 million–odd miles of surfaced highways, the railroad industry was more than holding its own.

With an aggressive modernization program which has cost them some $22 billion in the last 20 years, American railroads were operating at record levels in 1965. Although the old index of carloadings was down from previous levels, new, high-capacity cars and heavier loadings boosted revenue ton-miles to a new all-time peak of 695 billion, topping for the first time the 20-year-old war-time record of 681 billion set in 1945.

Back in March, 1944, Ford, Bacon & Davis celebrated its 50th anniversary, although many of the staff, scattered across the country on urgent jobs related to global war, could not attend. Mr. Bacon, then chairman, proposed a toast:

"To the engineering profession everywhere . . . in betterment of man's economic conditions the world around."

Some 22 years later, the president of the World Bank, George D. Woods, emphasizing the worldwide need for additional development capital, echoed the same point:

"Technology is not the toy of the prosperous. It is, potentially, the servant of all societies trying to engineer an escape from their poverty."

In 1965 U.S. industry valued its assets abroad at upwards of $90 billion and was investing additional capital in foreign enterprise at a yearly rate which totalled over $6 billion in 1964. By then, annual income on these investments had reached more than $5.1 billion, and was increasing.

Thus, with aggressive investment in new capacity, and accelerating advances in the technology of low-cost production, the American conquest of the human condition moves steadily ahead, creating new wealth not only for some 200 million Americans, but for countless millions of other peoples throughout the Free World.

Over the past 70-odd years, Ford, Bacon & Davis has made significant contributions in America's increasingly-successful war on poverty. Measured in capital involved, these engineering achievements are valued at many billions of dollars.

Applied to the challenges that lie ahead, however, accumulated technology and know-how, proved in successful experience, cannot be measured entirely in money. Far more importantly, they are the weapons that promise continuing success in man's unending struggle to wrest wealth from the earth, and shape it for human needs.

AFTERWORD

To each individual, the word "engineer" may well have a different meaning. At Ford, Bacon & Davis the concept of engineering is a broad one. To engineer is to conceive, plan, design, guide, construct and manage.

In this broad sense, financing, marketing, cost control or valuation, for example, are just as much a function of the engineer as the building of a hydro-electric installation or a 1,000-mile pipe line. The Ford, Bacon & Davis organization functions as engineer in the performance of each of the many interrelated services which are provided for clients. Its engineering approach to all problems is, by definition, objective, analytical, and practical—economically as well as functionally.

In other words, FB&D is a service organization. And at FB&D this means the performance of work for the benefit of others. If a client of Ford, Bacon & Davis does not receive specific, practical and valuable benefits from FB&D, the organization has failed in its primary responsibility.

Over the years, the Ford, Bacon & Davis record of service to business, industry, governments and institutions has created concrete evidence of value. The record shows this to be equally true in the case of relatively small assignments completed in a few weeks or months, and of major projects involving very large sums of money and covering a wide range of services over an extended period of time.

Since 1959, world headquarters of Ford, Bacon & Davis have occupied the entire 21st floor at 2 Broadway, New York, providing spacious offices, conference rooms, library, drafting and other facilities to handle a growing international business.

APPENDIX

PARTNERS, DIRECTORS

and

OFFICERS

of

FORD, BACON & DAVIS

FORD, BACON & DAVIS, INC.

and

FORD, BACON & DAVIS CONSTRUCTION CORPORATION

1894–1966

APPENDIX

FORD, BACON & DAVIS
PARTNERS

Frank R. Ford	1894–1921
George W. Bacon	1894–1921
George H. Davis	1896–1921
Charles N. Black	1912–1921
Charles F. Uebelacker	1912–1921
William von Phul	1912–1921

FORD, BACON & DAVIS, INC.
DIRECTORS

George W. Bacon	1921–1946
Charles N. Black	1921–1928
George H. Davis	1921–1942
Frank R. Ford	1921–1930
Charles F. Uebelacker	1921–1936
William von Phul	1921–1944
James A. Emery	1927–1943
John L. Esson	1929–1930
George I. Rhodes	1929–1949
James F. Towers	1929–1949
Edgar G. Hill	1930–1948
Schuyler C. Stivers	1931–1943
Page E. Golsan	1937–1945
Winfred E. Reynolds	1941–1947

DIRECTORS *(continued)*

Harry E. Whitaker	1941–1951
Everett S. Coldwell	1942–1959
Harold V. Coes	1943–1948
Cornelius J. Abbott	1944–1954
Henry F. Storck	1946–1956
Charles C. Whittelsey	1946–1966
David A. Uebelacker	1947–1964
Thomas I. Crowell	1949–1959
Benjamin E. Harris	1949–1957
Russell P. Westerhoff	1951–
William B. Poor	1955–
George O. Phillips	1956–
Carl S. Petrasch	1959–1962
Coleman R. Sample	1959–1962
George P. Breece	1962–
Stuart R. Fleming	1962–1965
Fred C. Culpepper, Jr.	1963–
William D. Bruce	1965–
Howard M. Hayes	1965–

CHAIRMEN OF THE BOARD

Charles F. Uebelacker	1921–1928
George W. Bacon	1928–1946
James F. Towers	1946–1949
Everett S. Coldwell	1949–1959
Charles C. Whittelsey	1959–1966
Russell P. Westerhoff	1966–

APPENDIX

APPENDIX

[201]

Behind this impressive facade at Monroe, La., Ford, Bacon & Davis Construction Corporation, a wholly-owned subsidiary, functions as headquarters for FB&D construction jobs involving pipe lines, electric generating stations and industrial facilities.

FORD, BACON & DAVIS CONSTRUCTION CORPORATION

DIRECTORS

George W. Bacon	1931–1946
George H. Davis	1931–1942
James A. Emery	1931–1943
Edgar G. Hill	1931–1948
George I. Rhodes	1931–1949
William von Phul	1931–1944
James F. Towers	1931–1949
Charles F. Uebelacker	1934–1936
Winfred E. Reynolds	1941–1947
Harry E. Whitaker	1942–1951
Page E. Golsan	1943–1945
Charles C. Whittelsey	1944–1966
Carl A. Schneider	1946–1948
Everett S. Coldwell	1946–1959
Cornelius J. Abbott	1947–1954
Henry F. Storck	1948–1956
David A. Uebelacker	1948–1964
Thomas I. Crowell, Jr.	1949–1959
Benjamin E. Harris	1949–1957
Russell P. Westerhoff	1951–
William B. Poor	1955–
George O. Phillips	1956–
Coleman R. Sample	1959–1962
Stuart R. Fleming	1962–1965
Fred C. Culpepper, Jr.	1963–

DIRECTORS *(continued)*

George P. Breece	1962–
Howard M. Hayes	1965–
John E. Baugh	1965–
William D. Bruce	1965–

CHAIRMEN OF THE BOARD

James F. Towers	1949–1949
Everett S. Coldwell	1949–1959
Charles C. Whittelsey	1959–1966
Russell P. Westerhoff	1966–

PRESIDENTS

Edgar G. Hill	1931–1948
James F. Towers	1948–1948
Everett S. Coldwell	1949–1957
Charles C. Whittelsey	1957–1965
George O. Phillips	1965–

EXECUTIVE VICE-PRESIDENTS

Charles C. Whittelsey	1948–1957
George O. Phillips	1958–1965

APPENDIX

APPENDIX

MEMBERS OF THE
25-YEAR CLUB
FORD, BACON & DAVIS, INC.
IN 1966

The 25-Year-Club was founded on the 50th anniversary of the business, and now includes all partners, officers and employees with a quarter-century of service in 1944 and following years:

ACTIVE

Abrams, Miss Marjorie R.	Josefowicz, Miss Regina V.
Antonelli, Peter	Kirk, Robert D.
Atkinson, John R.	Knutson, Clarence J.
Baldin, Lionel S.	Meagher, Mrs. Anna W.
Baugh, John E.	Miles, O. Landon
Callahan, Miss Elizabeth G.	Mount, John L., Jr.
Calkins, Miss Gertrude	Nugent, Mrs. Catherine C.
Craig, Roy W.	Phillips, George O.
Culpepper, Fred C., Jr.	Phillips, Francis A.
Dee, Richard P.	Schneider, Charles G.
Delaney, John J.	Sickels, Leroy H.
Durand, Eugene A.	Siedlecke, Miss Estelle
Erdman, Miss Elsie	Smith, Miss Adelaide
Fairley, Pat. H.	Smithson, Chester J.
Fischer, Miss Madeline M.	Sullivan, Miss Agnes N.
Fleury, Edward C.	Westerhoff, Russell P.
Henderson, John D.	Whitehead, Hardy
Jardine, Norman A.	Yeldell, Berry O.

MEMBERS OF THE
25-YEAR CLUB
FORD, BACON & DAVIS, INC.
IN 1966
(*continued*)

INACTIVE

Allen, Arthur C.

Coldwell, Everett S.

Conrad, Louis D.

Cooke, Charles B.

Dietze, Ferdinand H.

Drew, Newton

Drews, Henry C.

Ehrlich, Mrs. Muriel

Fleming, Stuart R.

Froidevaux, Bertram C.

Gilbert, Miss Gertrude

Golsan, Page E.

Goodman, Frederick T.

Harris, Miss Henrietta

Hatry, Miss Ida A.

Hill, Miss Selma M.

Lusk, William A.

Nelke, Mrs. Caroline P.

Nelke, Frank J.

Peterman, Lester C.

Rhodes, George I.

Roberts, Harvey E.

Rounds, Harold P.

Sample, Coleman R.

Sandford, Miss Elizabeth

Schnurer, Julius

Scott, Julien W.

Shumaker, Richard C.

Smith, William Thompson

Strong, Russell W.

Thomas, Mrs. Myrtle T.

Towers, James F.

von Phul, William, Jr.

Whitaker, Harry E.

Whittelsey, Charles C.

White, W. Arnold

MEMBERS OF THE
2 5 - Y E A R   C L U B
F O R D ,   B A C O N   &   D A V I S ,   I N C .
IN 1966
(*continued*)

DECEASED

Bacon, George W.
Bartlett, Samuel L.
Bertrand, Miss Lucy C.
Brown, Clinton B.
Carroll, Miss M. G.
Coes, Harold V.
Conrad, Miss Jessie M.
Cruikshank, Harold T.
Davis, George H.
Evans, Arthur J.
Grandin, Miss Evangeline
Greene, John F.
Harper, Charles H., Jr.
Harris, Benjamin E.
Hill, Edgar G.
Howlett, James B.
Kaase, William E.
Kingsbury, E. H.

McCallum, Miss Mary
Paine, Wilfred O.
Reynolds, Winfred E.
Ryan, Miss Elizabeth
Schneider, Carl A.
Smith, Ernest A.
Stivers, Schuyler C.
Storck, Henry F.
Taylor, Miss May M.
Timberlake, Seth M.
Trelease, Frank J.
Uebelacker, Armin A.
Uebelacker, David A.
von Phul, William
Wheeler, Bleecher L.
Wicks, Walter E.
Woods, John J.
Wright, William R.

Index

Page numbers in *italics* refer to illustrations.

[209]

INDEX

INDEX

INDEX

INDEX

INDEX

INDEX

Russia
J. P. Morgan & Co. and, 58
in World War I, 57
in World War II, 105

St. Charles Street Railway Company of New Orleans, 26–27
St. Francis Dam, rebuilding of, 56
St. Louis (Missouri), pipe lines to, 78, 79, 80
Salaries in 1930's, 89
Salt River Project, power service construction in, 154
Sample, Coleman R.
in Mexican surveys, 128
in valuation for Sinclair Oil Corp., 82
San Francisco (California)
earthquake reconstruction assignments in, 45
FB&D office in, 162
hydro-electric power for, 46
rapid transit system for, 63
Sanderson, Edwin N., 36
Sandwich (Illinois), pipe line to, 164
Sangamon Ordnance Plant, construction of, 112
Saskatchewan, Fort (Alberta), refinery construction at, 135
Schneider, Charles G., in Chilean mining studies, 175
Schultz, Robert S., Jr., in plant construction for F. S. Royster Guano Co., 123
Schwab, Charles M., Bethlehem Steel Corp. formed by, 37
Scioto Ordnance Plant, construction of, 112
Scranton (Pennsylvania), rail line to, 57
Sealright Company, investment in, 84
Seattle (Washington)
Boundary Project for, 182–183
power service construction for, 154
Securities and Exchange Act of 1933, 101
Seoul (Korea), 141
Shell Oil of Canada, valuation for, 127
Shell Oil Corporation, pipe line construction for, 107
Sherman, John, income tax denounced by, 23
Sherritt-Gordon Mines, Ltd., Lynn Lake project for, 135
Shoe industry and vulcanized rubber, 24
Sierra & San Francisco Power Company, management of, 46
Sierra Mountains, dam construction in, 46
Sinclair Oil Corporation, valuation for, 82
Sixteenth Amendment to Constitution, 52
Sloan, Alfred P., Jr., business guidelines of, 39

Smith, Beverly, 91
Smith and Corona Typewriters, Inc., L. C., investment in, 84
Societe Nationale de Transport et de Commercialisation des Hydrocarbures (SONATRACH), tariff studies for, 183, 185
South Carolina Public Service Authority, power plant construction for, 154
Southern Gas & Fuel Company, pipe line construction for, 77–78
Southern Natural Gas Company, pipe line construction for, 79, 151, 162, 179
Spain, 161
steel engineering studies in, 159, 175
Spanish-American War, 32
Spindletop oil well, 37
Stalingrad (Russia), battle of, 105
Standard of living, see Economic activity
Standard Oil Company, dissolution ordered by Supreme Court, 51
Standard Oil Company of California, appraisal for, 67
Standard Oil Company of Kentucky, pipe line construction for, 107
Standard Oil Company of New Jersey
natural gas survey for, 77
pipe line construction for, 107, 179
valuation for, 81
Standard Oil Company of Ohio, feasibility study for, 151–152
Steel industry
growth of, 37, 98, 188–189
J. P. Morgan's consolidation of, 36
See also names of steel companies
Steel production
in 1894, 24
in 1920's, 73
in 1939, 105
in 1940, 105
in World War I period, 58
Sterlington (Louisiana), power station construction for, 74
Stivers, Schuyler C., association with FB&D, 42
Stock control in FB&D, 137
Stock market
in 1893, 21
in 1901, 35
in 1920's, 72
in 1929 collapse, 87
in Korean War period, 141
Stone, Charles A., 36
Storage reservoirs for natural gas, 131, 133–134
Storck, Henry F., Tenure Plan devised by, 137

Index

FOR HUMAN NEEDS

The Story of Ford, Bacon & Davis

The text of this book is set in Linotype Baskerville. It is 12 point with 3 points of leading. The chapter titles are 18 point Bulmer.

The book is printed on 70 pound Perkins & Squier paper from offset plates. The cloth binding is Columbia Colonial Vellum.

Typographic design and layout is by Sidney Feinberg. The book was composed, printed and bound by American Book–Stratford Press, Inc., at its plant in New York, New York.

NATIONAL AERONAUTICS AND SPACE ADMINISTRATION
MANNED SPACECRAFT CENTER

FLIGHT ACCELERATION FACILITY

Ford, Bacon & Davis
Incorporated